Judgment of the Nephilim

Study Guide

Ryan Pitterson

MEET RYAN PITTERSON

Thank you for joining me on this study! One of the greatest blessings of being an author is attending conferences and events where I can meet and speak with readers. Your feedback and passion for the Bible is a true inspiration to me.

Ryan Pitterson is a Biblical researcher and writer with an emphasis on ancient Hebrew thought and theology. He received his B.A. in Political Science from the University of Rochester and his JD from Columbia Law School.

One of the most common questions I have been asked is: *"Will you ever make a study guide or workbook?"* Because of the nature of the research that goes into writing **Judgment Of The Nephilim** and **The Final Nephilim**, The Lord has provided a great deal of information to take in and learn. So it's only fitting that we have a Companion Study Guide that can help you process the information, truly understand the concepts and learn in a group setting.

So to all the readers who have asked this question or just want to get deeper in their study - **this book is dedicated to you**. It's my honor to assist you as we all grow in the knowledge of our Lord and Savior Jesus Christ.

CONTENTS

1. THE ULTIMATE PROPHECY

CHAPTERS 1-2

Genesis 3:15 is the foundation of the entire Bible. All Scripture rests on the promise of The Messiah - a child born of a human woman, who would one day defeat Satan and redeem humanity. As you work through this section, keep this prophecy at the forefront of your thinking.

KEY THEMES:

- The unique creation of humanity and its effect on the angelic realm.
- Satan's plan to corrupt mankind in order to prevent the human race from replacing the fallen angels.
- The spiritual attacks on Adam and Eve, Cain and Lamech reveal the Devil's hatred of the family and his mission to make us doubt God's love for us.
- The Lord provides endless mercy to us when we fall into sinful temptation.

HUMANITY – GOD'S SPECIAL CREATION

1. Read Job 38:4-7. How can we know that the angels were created *before* humanity and thus witnessed our creation?

"Sang with Joy at the creation of planet earth"
Job 38

2. What were 3 things about human beings that made us uniquely special and distinct from angels?

1 Stewards of Earth
2 Marriage
3 Sex!

WHAT MAKES YOU SO SPECIAL

"So God created man in his own image, in the image of God created he him; male and female created he them."

Genesis 1:27

Though it's not often taught in churches and seminaries, Job 38:4-7 tells us conclusively that angels witnessed the creation of the Earth. Not only did they see this, but they also rejoiced and sang songs of praise as The Lord formed the planet we inhabit in all of its glorious splendor. This necessarily means that angels also witnessed the creation of humanity. And they heard the Divine proclamation of the Godhead to make man "in our own image."

This made humanity an altogether unique creation – as we were chosen to bear God's image. You are unique in creation - God made you in his image. When Jesus rescued Shadrach, Meshach, and Abednego from the fiery furnace, King Nebuchadnezzar exclaimed: "...I see four ***men*** loose, walking in the midst of the fire..." (Daniel 3:25). The book of Hebrews states of Christ's incarnation: "For verily he took not on him the nature of angels; but he took on him the seed of Abraham" (Hebrews 2:16). Even before His incarnation on Earth, Jesus Christ looked like a man, or more aptly, humans resemble Jesus Christ.

You not only have His traits but when you believe in Him you take on His spirit. From childhood, the world bombards us with messages that attempt to tell us how we should define our value as a human being. Whether it's personal appearance, beauty, wealth, achievements, strength, family name or social media "likes", there are endless ways society offers to define our "value." But when we put our faith and trust in The Lord Jesus Christ, it is He who defines our worth. As an image-bearer of the Creator of The Universe, you were born with a value nothing in the world can match. When Jesus Christ came to earth at His first Advent, we are told:

> "For he shall grow up before him as a tender plant, and as a root out of a
> dry ground: he hath no form nor comeliness; and when we shall see him,
> there is no beauty that we should desire him."

Isaiah 53:2

As the son of a carpenter in the lower economic class, Jesus had no worldly "status" to speak of. On a number of occasions, He was criticized for His perceived lack of "prestige":

> "And Nathanael said unto him, Can there any good thing come out of Nazareth?"

John 1:46

Notice the reaction of the people when Jesus taught:

> "And when the sabbath day was come, he began to teach in the synagogue: and
> many hearing him were astonished, saying, From whence hath this man these
> things? and what wisdom is this which is given unto him, that even such mighty
> works are wrought by his hands? **Is not this the carpenter**, the son of Mary, the
> brother of James, and Joses, and of Juda, and Simon? and are not his sisters here
> with us? And they were offended at him."

Mark 6:2-3

Oh, Jesus was much more than "the carpenter." Far more than those people could imagine at that time. And you are much more than your family name, or job, or school grades or social media popularity level. You are an image bearer of Jesus – created with love by the Almighty. Never forget how precious and special you are in God's eyes.

THE RELENTLESS ATTACKS OF THE ENEMY

> "And there appeared a great wonder in heaven; a woman clothed with the sun, and the moon under her feet, and upon her head a crown of twelve stars: And she being with child cried, travailing in birth, and pained to be delivered. And there appeared another wonder in heaven; and behold a great red dragon, having seven heads and ten horns, and seven crowns upon his heads. And his tail drew the third part of the stars of heaven, and did cast them to the earth: and the dragon stood before the woman which was ready to be delivered, for to devour her child as soon as it was born."
>
> **Revelation 12:1-4**

Revelation 12 opens with the Apostle John receiving a chilling vision in the sky: a woman "clothed with the sun" – symbolizing the nation of Israel, giving birth to the Seed of the Woman – the Messiah. While the birth of this child is glorious, the Enemy soon appears. The Devil, in the form of a Dragon, attempts to kill the child as soon as it was born. This is a picture of Satan's relentless attacks on all who oppose him. Thankfully, God provides us with the ways to ward off the enemy and stand strong in Him.

3. What was the spiritual purpose of the Garden of Eden? What was the significance of Adam being told to "keep" the Garden?

4. Why was the marriage of Adam and Eve such a revolutionary event? What is the spiritual symbolism of marriage?

5. "And when the woman saw that the tree _____

_____

_____, she took of the fruit thereof, and did eat, and gave also unto her husband with her; and he did eat." - Genesis 3:6

6. Read Numbers 21:6 and 2 Corinthians 11:14. Identify the terms in each that translate to *saraph* in Hebrew. What does this tell us about Satan's appearance in Genesis 3?

7. Read Exodus 34:27-33. With Moses' experience in view, what could have changed about Adam and Eve's appearance once they sinned?

8. Thinking about Genesis 3:15, what was the significance for: 1) humanity 2)

God 3) the Devil and the fallen angels? what does this prophecy mean to you in terms of how you view the Bible and your relationship with God?

9. From the <u>fallen angelic perspective</u>, what was important about Cain's birth?

10. Reading Ephesians 6:12, list 3 of the true enemies of humanity? What does this mean for how you should treat people you interact with in your life?

11. Read Revelation 12:1-4. 1) How does this relate back to the Garden of Eden? 2) What was the significance of Adam naming his wife "Eve"? 3) What is the spiritual significance of marriage in light of the war of the two bloodlines?

The Garden of Eden was the original temple between God and humanity, and Adam was its priest. It was the portal between the heavenly and earthly realms. Giving Adam control over the Garden and dominion over the entire earth sent shockwaves through fallen angelic realm. It is important to note that when we read Genesis chapter 3, Satan is already evil. Just as the angels were created before humanity, so did the original angelic rebellion and fall of the Devil take place before the creation of mankind. Ezekiel 28 reveals that Satan was once the High Priest in the Garden of Eden:

> "Son of man, take up a lamentation upon the king of Tyrus, and say unto him, Thus saith the Lord GOD; Thou sealest up the sum, full of wisdom, and perfect in beauty. **Thou hast been in Eden the garden of God**; every precious stone was thy covering, the sardius, topaz, and the diamond, the beryl, the onyx, and the jasper, the sapphire, the emerald, and the carbuncle, and gold: the workmanship of thy tabrets and of thy pipes was prepared in thee in the day that thou wast created."
>
> **Ezekiel 28:12-13**

This amazing, esoteric passage reveals some of the earliest history of the Adversary. We see that Satan was once in the Garden, decked with jewels that match those that God designated for Aaron, the first the High Priest of Israel:

> "And thou shalt make the breastplate of judgment with cunning work; after the work of the ephod thou shalt make it; of gold, of blue, and of purple, and of scarlet, and of fine twined linen, shalt thou make it. Foursquare it shall be being doubled; a span shall be the length thereof, and a span shall be the breadth thereof. And thou shalt set in it settings of stones, even four rows of stones: the first row shall be a sardius, a topaz, and a carbuncle: this shall be the first row.
>
> And the second row shall be an emerald, a sapphire, and a diamond. And the third row a ligure, an agate, and an amethyst. And the fourth row a beryl, and an onyx, and a jasper: they shall be set in gold in their inclosings. And the stones shall be with the names of the children of Israel, twelve, according to their names, like the engravings of a signet; every one with his name shall they be according to the twelve tribes."
>
> **Exodus 28:15-21**

The angelic priestly breastplate only had 9 stones, but they were all later included in the 12 jewels assigned for the breastplate of the High Priest of Israel. So imagine the shock to see the Garden and the Earth the Devil once had dominion over transferred to Adam. And on top of this, Adam was given a wife – Eve. Angels were forbidden to marry and thus do not procreate. But Adam and Eve were instructed by The Lord to "be fruitful and multiply."

If Adam, this seemingly inferior creature, could usurp Lucifer, then all humans *could eventually replace the fallen angels* in the Heavenly Order. And this was a threat. This is what initiated the attack on Adam and Eve to lure them into rebellion against God. By deceiving Eve into violating the one prohibition God gave the first 2 humans, Satan could demonstrate that humanity was "just as guilty" as he was and worthy of The Lord's wrath.

What the Devil did not anticipate was that in marriage there was a powerful foreshadow of God's plan of redemption for fallen humanity. The Lord, of course being omniscient, anticipated the Enemy's strike and prepared a plan to forgive and reconcile with sinful humanity. Much more than a pledge of love between a man and a woman, marriage was a "mystery":

> "Husbands, love your wives, even as Christ also loved the church, and gave himself for it… For this cause shall a man leave his father and mother, and shall be joined unto his wife, and they two shall be one flesh. This is a great mystery: but I speak concerning Christ and the church."
>
> **Ephesians 5:23-25, 31–32**

This "mystery" – revealed in the church age – is that marriage itself is a type and shadow of the spiritual relationship between Jesus Christ the Bridegroom, and His Church – all born-again Christians, who are spiritually "the Bride of Christ."

And in the marriage of Adam and Eve there would come a child – the Seed of the Woman – Messiah. Even in pronouncing punishment, The Lord declared the

Ultimate Prophecy – the birth of The Redeemer. One day a son would be born who would save mankind and "crush" the head of the Serpent. This set the course of history for the next 6,000 years. The Devil from that point on was determined to destroy, corrupt or prevent the birth of this child. This is why Cain was such a target. From the fallen angelic perspective, Cain could have been the Messiah. He was after all, the first "Seed of the Woman." Thus, his destruction was of paramount importance to the fallen angels. And by luring him into the heinous act of murdering his own brother, the Devil in effect was able to kill "2 potential messiahs with one stone."

The fallen angels and demons- true enemies of born-again Christians, are relentless in their attacks. In Ephesians 6, the Apostle Paul describes the battle against them as "wrestling":

> "Put on the whole armour of God, that ye may be able to stand against the wiles of the devil. For we wrestle not against flesh and blood, but against principalities, against powers, against the rulers of the darkness of this world, against spiritual wickedness in high places. Wherefore take unto you the whole armour of God, that ye may be able to withstand in the evil day, and having done all, to stand."
>
> **Ephesians 6:11-13**

Paul, no doubt well aware of the original Olympic games that took place in ancient Greece, compared out spiritual battle against the fallen angelic realm as a wrestling match, a struggle in which two combatants look arms and use all their strength to knock their opponent to the ground. Twice he exhorts us to "put on the whole armour of God" – emphasizing that this is serious warfare. Never forget how relentless the Devil and his minions are in their attacks on the human race. You cannot fight the battle alone and it is futile to try. But the armour of God is what we need to protect ourselves:

> "Stand therefore, having your loins girt about with truth, and having on the breastplate of righteousness; And your feet shod with the preparation of the

gospel of peace; Above all, taking the shield of faith, wherewith ye shall be able to quench all the fiery darts of the wicked. And take the helmet of salvation, and the sword of the Spirit, which is the word of God: Praying always with all prayer and supplication in the Spirit, and watching thereunto with all perseverance and supplication for all saints;"

Ephesians 6:14-18

It takes truth, righteousness, the Gospel, faith, salvation and the Word of God to "quench all the fiery darts of the wicked." Studying the Bible, sharing the Gospel, living a righteous life for Christ and a consistent and fervent prayer life provide the armour Christians need daily to defend ourselves from the attacks of the enemy. We are spiritually at our weakest and most prone to commit our most besetting sins when we have gone too long a time without serious Bible study and prayer. Commit to live a spirit-filled life and you will be able to stand.

FEEL GOD'S LOVE

12. How would you rate your "spiritual strength" in your day-to-day battles with sin, stress, fear and the challenges of life?

1   2   3   4   5   6   7   8   9   10

13. What are some things you can commit to in order to improve your strength and spiritual armor?

14. Complete the verses below

God's great plan for humanity

"Fear not, little flock; for it is _____

_____" - Luke 12:32

God's forgiveness

"For thou, Lord, _____

_____unto all them that call upon thee." -Psalm 86:5

The Messiah

"For _____: and the

government shall be upon his shoulder: and his name shall be called

Wonderful, Counsellor, The mighty God, The everlasting Father, The Prince

of Peace." - Isaiah 9:6

The schemes of the enemy

"Be sober, be vigilant; because your adversary_____

_____" - 1 Peter 5:8

15. How did you see these attributes in your Walk with God?

2.   ENTER THE SONS OF GOD
CHAPTERS 3-4

Genesis 6:4 is one of the most debated verses in the Bible. The majority of churches teach that the "Sons of God" were faithful, human men who married sinful, non-believing women. So much of the understanding of Old Testament history rests on properly identifying who the Sons of God truly are - fallen angels who, in lust, corrupted the human genetic code before the Flood.

KEY THEMES:

- Since the first century AD, the Church understood that the "Sons of God" were angels, not men.
- Genesis 6 details literal fornication leading to the birth of the Nephilim.
- The lineage of Cain serves as a tragic example of a father's rejection of God having dire consequences for future generations. Our sins greatly affect the ones we love.

1. Read Genesis 4:1-3, Genesis 4:14 and Genesis 6:1. How do these verses establish the timeline of events in Genesis 6:4?

2. When the Bible says "there were giants in the earth in those days; and also after that..." what is "after that" referring to? Where is the Biblical confirmation of this?

3. What is the Hebrew translation of "Sons of God"? what is unique about its usage in the Old Testament?

4. Explain Dr. Michael Heiser's reasoning on the translation of "Sons of God"

5. What are 2 ways we can confirm the meaning of "Sons of God" from Job chapters 1, 2 and 38?

6. "Beloved, now _____, and it
doth not yet appear what we shall be: but we know that, when he shall appear,
_____." - 1 John 3:2

WHO WERE THE SONS OF GOD? THE GREAT DEBATE

The entire supernatural interpretation of Genesis 6, the understanding of the Great Flood, the wars in Canaan and much of the entire Bible itself rests on the question: who were "the sons of God" of Genesis 6? If they were merely God-fearing human men, then much of what we understand about the nature of God becomes a lot more difficult to explain. Why would a loving God wipe out the entire human population save for 8 people in the days of Noah? Why would The Lord order the extermination of men, women and children in the wars of the land of Canaan? These are difficult questions that many atheists, Bible skeptics and those who are genuinely curious about the Christian faith raise on a daily basis. And they are good questions, because at first glance, those harsh judgments fly in the face of everything we believe and share about the goodness, love, empathy and mercy of our Lord Jesus Christ.

However, when we understand the literal interpretation of Genesis 6 – that the Sons of God, the *b'nai ha Elohim* in Scripture, were fallen angels who committed one of the most dangerous and deadly attacks on humanity, pushing us to the brink of utter extinction and jeopardizing any chance for redemption – then God's response in the days of Noah and in the land of Canaan start to make perfect sense. Rather than these being irrational, harsh judgments from the "angry God of the Old Testament" they were just 2 of the numerous examples of Yahweh displaying His love by rescuing mankind from utter destruction.

The Book of Job provides the confirmation of the supernatural interpretation because outside of Genesis 6, it is the only Old Testament book that contains the phrase *b'nai ha Elohim*, or "the Sons of God." And letting Scripture interpret Scripture, we are given a clear definition – they were indeed angels.

> "Now there was a day when the sons of God came to present themselves
> before the LORD, and Satan came also among them. And the LORD said
> unto Satan, Whence comest thou? Then Satan answered the LORD, and
> said, From going to and fro in the earth, and from walking up and down in
> it."
>
> **Job 1:6–7**

This passage details God's literal meeting with the sons of God in Heaven. This is, to use a term popularized by Dr. Heiser, a "Divine Council" in which God presides over an assembly of holy and fallen angels to discuss worldly affairs, grant permission to carry out certain actions in the human realm, or assign various tasks.

Job 2 describes another Divine Council. The third reference to the sons of God in the Old Testament is also in the book of Job, in chapter 38. When God was posing questions to Job about the creation of the universe (to show Job how little understanding and knowledge he had compared to the Lord), He proclaimed:

> "Where wast thou when I laid the foundations of the earth? declare, if thou
> hast understanding. Who hath laid the measures thereof, if thou knowest?
> or who hath stretched the line upon it? Whereupon are the foundations
> thereof fastened? or who laid the corner stone thereof; When the morning
> stars sang together, and all the sons of God [*b'nai ha Elohim*] shouted for
> joy?"
>
> **Job 38:4–7**

Thus, the sons of God were not only in the presence of the Lord but existed even before the earth itself was created. Every use of the term *b'nai ha Elohim* in the Old Testament refers to angelic beings. The use of the phrase in the New Testament (which was written in Greek) has the same meaning.

Examining the use of the term *Elohim* in Scripture from a linguistic perspective leads to the same conclusion. Dr. Michael S. Heiser, adjunct Professor of Biblical Studies at Liberty University, who holds a PhD in Hebrew and Semitic studies, writes:

> "All beings called Elohim in the Hebrew Bible share a certain characteristic: they all inhabit the non – human realm. By nature, Elohim are not part of the world of humankind, the world of ordinary embodiment. Elohim – as a term – indicates residence, not a set of attributes; it identifies the proper domain of the entity it describes. Yahweh, the lesser gods of His council, angels, demons, and the disembodied dead all inhabit the spiritual world. They may cross over into the human world – as the Bible informs us – and certain humans may be transported to the non-human realm (e.g., prophets; Enoch). But the proper domains of each are two separate and distinct places." – The Divine Council, Dr. Michael Heiser. http://www.thedivinecouncil.com/ElohimAsGodsFSB.pdf

SATAN'S NUCLEAR STRIKE ON THE HUMAN RACE

With the human population expanding, the Devil could no longer rely on the strategy of corrupting or killing one potential Messiah at a time. Cain's banishment from Eden allowed the Godly line to continue and flourish unabated through Seth, the third son of Adam and Eve. Thus, with the hundreds of potential Messiahs being born, it would take a large-scale attack to thwart The Lord's plan of redemption through a human son. This is what instigated a faction of the fallen angels to enter the human realm and take human women as wives. Fueled by jealousy of humanity, these angels rebelled against God in order to partake in marriage and fornication, becoming the fathers of the Nephilim. Their incursion threatened to corrupt human DNA and the prophecy of a human child redeeming mankind.

A 19th century Christian theologian also took this view:

> "...the angels of [Genesis 6:2] were instigated by Satan to the commission of their sin, in order that he might thus be enabled to effect what we may, not inappropriately term, the adulteration of the Adamite race- that the race, for the salvation of which the promised seed of the woman should come, should be no longer purely Adam's, but a race impured and mixed - partly of demonic origin - attempting thus to overthrow the counsel, and defeat the purpose of God." - *The Fallen Angels and Heroes of Mythology*, Reverend John Fleming, Dublin: Hodges, Foster and Figgis, 1879, p. 132.

Additionally, going back to the 1st century in Judea, we find the Jewish historian Josephus arriving at the same conclusion:

> "For many Angels of God accompanied with women, and begat sons that proved unjust, and despisers of all that was good; on account of the confidence they had in their own strength. For the tradition is, that these men did what resembled the acts of those whom the Grecians call *Giants*." - Josephus, *Antiquities*, Chapter 3.

The church fathers from Justin Martyr to Tertullian all held to the supernatural interpretation of Genesis 6. This was the common understanding in the church and ancient Jewish community for millennia.

BORN AGAIN BELIEVERS WILL BE THE NEW "SONS OF GOD"

> "But as many as received him, to them gave he power to become the sons of God, even to them that believe on his name"
>
> **John 1:12**

Salvation in Christ is not just spiritual, it is physical and genetic. A born-again Christian not only receives a new spirit - born of God. They also receive an immortal, heavenly realm body - like Christ received at His resurrection. Just as the Enemy wants to corrupt human genetics, Christ redeems human genetics by replacing our sinful flesh, with a sinless, heavenly body.

THE FIRST FAMILY OF THE NEPHILIM

"Blessed is the man that walketh not in the counsel of the ungodly, nor standeth in the way of sinners, nor sitteth in the seat of the scornful."

Psalm 1:1

Genesis 4 contains a cautionary tale on the dangers of living a life apart from God. Once Cain was banished from Eden, his descendants were not only geographically removed from the first temple in paradise, but they were also spiritually removed – living for generations with no repentance, reverence or worship of God. By the seventh generation from Adam through Cain's lineage, we find a family so immersed in sinful rebellion they were the perfect target for Satan's next strike in his ongoing battle to undo the Ultimate Prophecy.

7. What is a "special reference" in the Bible? What is Scripture telling us when it uses one?

8. What were 3 traits of Lamech that made him a target for the fallen angels?

9. Explain the spiritual signifignce of the name Tubal-Cain? How can spiritual choices of parents affect their children?

10. What technological advances did Lamech's family receive from the apostate Sons of God?

11. List 2 Early church sources that wrote about Naamah. What was their specific understanding about her role in Genesis 6?

12. After the Bible details the generation of Lamech's Children, his genealogy abruptly ends. What could have been the reason for this?

13. What does Lamech's sin say about our desire for material wealth and worldly approval? How can you improve in avoiding these sins (love of money, jealousy, social media approval, covetousness, etc.) in your own walk with God?

THE DEVIL IN THE DETAILS

Much of the beauty of the Bible resides in its divinely inspired smallest details. How easy is it to read the genealogies in the books of Genesis with a cursory glance and move quickly to "the good stuff" of Scripture? However, these genealogies tell a story – THE story – of the Bible. They stand as a running testimony and evidence of God's protection of the lineage that would lead to the Messiah and salvation. Some genealogies, however, chronicle *the generations of the wicked* and we find an example in Genesis 4 with the descendants of Cain. God, in His wisdom, created "special references" – portions of a lineage where several verses are devoted to describing a single patriarch or generation in order for us to take note that this person holds an infamous place in ancient Biblical history.

Lamech was one of these men. A literal reading of Scripture points to Cain's descendant Lamech and his immediate family as the first humans to interact and interbreed with the fallen angels who invaded Earth and fathered the antediluvian Nephilim.

In the opening verses detailing his generation we see that Lamech was a polygamist – and the first person on record to violate Yahweh's marital covenant of one man and one woman cleaved eternally:

> "And Lamech took unto him two wives: the name of the one was Adah,
> and the name of the other Zillah."
> ### Genesis 4:19

Note that the Lamech "took" his two wives. The Hebrew word *laqah*, is the same verb used to describe the Sons of God in Genesis 6 when they "took" the daughters of men as brides:

> "That the sons of God saw the daughters of men that they were fair; and
> *they took them wives* of all which they chose."
> ### Genesis 6:2

In addition to being a polygamist, Lamech was a murderer:

"And Lamech said unto his wives, Adah and Zillah, Hear my voice; ye
wives of Lamech, hearken unto my speech: for I have slain a man to
my wounding, and a young man to my hurt. If Cain shall be avenged
sevenfold, truly Lamech seventy and sevenfold."

Genesis 4:23–24

He not only boasted to his wives of murdering a man, but he also mocked the merciful
protection God gave Cain after he slew Abel by proclaiming: "If Cain shall be avenged
sevenfold, truly Lamech seventy and sevenfold." His arrogance and violence indicate a man
who had no reverence for the Creator. In fact, unlike Adam, Eve and Cain - Lamech did not
receive an immediate punishment from God for his polygamy or killing a man. This likely
further emboldened him in his evil as Scripture confirms is often the case:

"Because sentence against an evil work is not executed speedily, therefore the heart
of the sons of men is fully set in them to do evil."

Ecclesiastes 8:11

This rebellious heart provided the perfect soil for the Enemy to plant seeds of even greater
sin – engaging with the fallen angels. Genesis 4 not only provides a detailed description of
Lamech, but it also chronicles all four of his children, something not found in any other
lineage in the early chapters of Genesis. And when we examine the lives of his sons there is
a technological explosion:

"And Adah bare Jabal: he was the father of such as dwell in tents, and of such as
have cattle. And his brother's name was Jubal: he was the father of all such as
handle the harp and organ. And Zillah, she also bare Tubal Cain, an instructer of
every artificer in brass and iron…"

Genesis 4:20-22

Consider the advances in this one family. Jabal was the father of animal husbandry and tent-
making. Jubal invented musical instruments. And Tubal-Cain (who was named after his
wicked forefather Cain) was the father of blacksmithing and metallurgy. Most of the basic

technology of ancient society was invented by this one family. How were they able to do this? By receiving hidden knowledge from the fallen angels.

A renowned 18th-century sermon confirmed that the descendants of Cain were the first humans the angels mingled with:

> "The fall of the Angels here alluded to losing them their first [estate] could not be their Pride and Ambition. That was aspiring above them. This is rather described as a degeneracy and falling short of the dignity and excellency of their Nature which was exactly this ignoble sort of Marriages **whereby they mingled this Holy Seed of God with the unholy Posterity of the piacular Cain.**" – *A Sermon Preach'd at Chester: Against Marriages in Different Communions*, Charles Leslie, Henry Dodwell, Printed by W.B. for Char. Brome at the West End of St. Paul's, 1702, p. 165.

This was the transaction – divine knowledge in exchange for a woman's hand in marriage. And that first woman is also mentioned by name in Genesis 4:

> "and the sister of Tubal Cain was Naamah."
> **Genesis 4:22**

Naamah was the first bride of a fallen angel and mother of the Nephilim. She is the only "sister" mentioned in any genealogy in the Bible. In the 1,656-year history of the pre-flood world only 4 women are mentioned by name: Eve and the three women in Lamech's family – Adah, Zillah and Naamah. Her name in Hebrew means "beauty" – and it is clear that beauty drove the fallen angels to act upon their jealousy of the marital covenant The Lord gave to humanity.

Early church sources identified Naamah as the first mother of the Nephilim. Professor Robert Jenkin, writing in 1721, described Naamah as the first woman to "entice the sons of God." The Rainbow, a 19th century Christian magazine, arrived at the same conclusion:

> "He had also a daughter Naamah, who was beautiful, but she was not to be the mother of the promised seed, but rather the fountain whence sprang

much of that fairness among the daughters of men, which not long after tempted the angels to "go after strange flesh" and brought on their defection from God and the fearful corruption of the world before the Flood."– *Satan's Parody of God's Kingdom*, as printed in The Rainbow, a Magazine of Christian Literature, Vol. XX, 1883, p. 438.

This is where the Nephilim were born. Further evidence of this fact is that after the generation of Lamech's children, his genealogy abruptly ends. We see no further mention of Cain's descendants even though the Flood judgment would not come for several more centuries. Why? Because this was the last generation that was fully human.

3.   THE AGE OF ENOCH

CHAPTER 5-6

Enoch was the first person to proclaim a prophecy from God. He lived in a time when the fallen angels first took human wives entering the human realm at the Jordan River. This incursion took place in the family of his contemporary, Lamech. His faith in The Lord and bold witness to the world was rewarded with him being raptured - making him the first person to never die.

KEY THEMES:

- There are many writings on Enoch but the Bible carries the true account of this man of God.
- The Jordan River, site of numerous supernatural events in the Bible, was the location where the fallen Sons of God entered the human realm to take human women as wives.
- Enoch and Noah were the only 2 men in the Bible who "walked with God." Enoch's faith is an example for all believers today.
- The world attempts to offer solutions to all of our problems but these are all poor substitutes for the peace and joy that comes from Jesus Christ.

THE "AREA 51" OF THE ANCIENT WORLD

Where did the fallen angels arrive on earth? What was the location of the portal that allowed the Sons of God to enter the human realm in the days of Noah? The Book of Enoch cites Mount Hermon as the original landing point for the rebellious Watcher angels who would become the fathers of the Nephilim. But was this the case? The Bible gives no indication that Mt. Hermon was the "landing point" for the angelic invaders of the antediluvian world. Many passages in Scripture point instead to the Jordan River as being the far more likely location for the sons of God who left their first estate to fornicate with human women. The Jordan River was the "Area 51" of the ancient world, as numerous supernatural events took place in its waters and on its shores. It served as an ancient portal between the heavenly and earthly realms and a significant location for the Nephilim in Scripture.

1. What is the Hebrew translation of the name "Jordan"? What is the relevance of this translation for this study?

2. What distinguishes the Jordan river from Mt. Hermon in Scripture?

3. Name 3 supernatural events that took place at the Jordan river. How do they relate to the Genesis 6 incursion?

4. Read Matthew 3:13-17. How does the account of Jesus' baptism help support the notion of the Genesis 6 angels' "landing Spot" for their incursion?

In recent years, *Judgment Of The Nephilim* has helped spark the debate about what was the true "landing spot" for the Genesis 6 apostate angels. Why does this matter? Because the Bible is the only divinely inspired text in existence and as such, Christians have a duty to make sure that anything coming from outside of Scripture is in agreement with the Holy Word. Time and time again, the location of supernatural activity in the ancient world was the Jordan river, giving much more credence to it being the location of the portal between the heavenly and earthly realms.

The first clue can be found in its name. Jordan, or *Yarden* in Hebrew means "the place of their descent" or "their going down." It is mentioned 179 times in the Bible – far more than Mt. Hermon. It also was the site to numerous supernatural events:

- When Abraham's grandson Jacob was in Bethel, due west of the Jordan River, he saw in his dream *angels ascending and descending* on a ladder and God standing above it (Genesis 28:12).

- The prophet Elijah was supernaturally fed meat and bread by ravens (who are carnivorous animals) at the brook Cherith – a brook of the Jordan river. (1 Kings 17:1-6).

- Elijah later returned to the Jordan River to be literally transported to Heaven by God:

"And the sons of the prophets that were at Jericho came to Elisha, and said unto him, Knowest thou that the LORD will take away thy master from thy head to day? And he answered, Yea, I know it; hold ye your peace. And Elijah said unto him, Tarry, I pray thee, here; *for the LORD hath sent me to Jordan.* And he said, As the LORD liveth, and as thy soul liveth, I will not leave thee. And they two went on. And fifty men of the sons of the prophets went, and stood to view afar off: **and they two stood by Jordan**. And Elijah took his mantle, and wrapped it together, and smote the waters, and they were divided hither and thither, so that they two went over on dry ground. And it came to pass, when they were gone over, that Elijah said unto Elisha, Ask what I shall do for thee, before I be taken away from thee. And Elisha said, I pray thee, let a double   portion of thy spirit be upon me. And he said, Thou hast asked a hard thing: nevertheless, if thou see me when I am taken from thee, it shall be so unto thee; but if not, it shall not be so. **And it came to pass, as they still went on, and talked, that, behold, there appeared a chariot of fire, and horses of fire, and parted them both asunder; and Elijah went up by a whirlwind into heaven.**"

2 Kings 2:5–11

By divine power Elijah and Elisha crossed over the Jordan River on dry ground, as the waters supernaturally parted for them to pass through. Angelic chariots and horses then took Elijah up into Heaven at the Jordan River, giving further evidence that there was some form of divine portal or passageway at this river.

Naaman, the Syrian military commander, was miraculously healed of leprosy (a death sentence in the ancient world), after the prophet Elisha instructed him to dip himself in the waters of the Jordan river 7 times.

But the greatest example of the supernatural portal between Heaven and earth at the Jordan river was at the baptism of The Lord Jesus Christ:

"**Then cometh Jesus from Galilee to Jordan** unto John, to be baptized of him. But John forbad him, saying, I have need to be baptized of thee, and comest thou to me? And Jesus answering said unto him, Suffer it to be so now: for thus it becometh us to fulfil all righteousness. Then he suffered him. And Jesus, when he was baptized, went up straightway out of the water: **and, lo, the heavens were opened unto him, and he saw the**

Spirit of God descending like a dove, and lighting upon him: And lo a voice from heaven, saying, This is my beloved Son, in whom I am well pleased."

Matthew 3:13–17

Jesus Christ, God in the flesh, chose to be baptized in the Jordan River. And the skies opened to reveal a heavenly portal and the Holy Spirit *descended on Him* in the same divinely appointed location of the Jordan River. Immediately after this, God the Father spoke from Heaven to Earth for all to hear proclaiming that Jesus Christ was the Son of God. The pathway from Earth to the divine realm was on display at this mystical river.

5. Read Matthew 3:5-9. What was the significance of the stones and their location (Also see Joshua 4:1-11)?

6. What is another name for the river "Hiddekel"? What happened to Daniel there (Daniel 10:1-7)?

7. Read Ezekiel 1:1-7. What happened in the sky? What did Ezekiel see?

Though it's not as well-known as the parting of the Red Sea, there was another divine parting of waters at the Jordan river. When the 40-year wilderness punishment came to an end and it was time for the younger generation of Israelites to enter the Promised Land, God led the nation to the eastern shore of the Jordan river. There, Yahweh supernaturally parted the waters. This was done for a specific purpose – it was God's reassurance to His people that He was with them and would protect them through the wars in the land of Canaan:

"And Joshua said unto the children of Israel, Come hither, and hear the words of the LORD your God. **And Joshua said, Hereby ye shall know that the living God is among you, and that he will without fail drive out from before you the Canaanites, and the Hittites, and the Hivites, and the Perizzites, and the Girgashites, and the Amorites, and the Jebusites.** Behold, the ark of the covenant of the LORD of all the earth passeth over before you into Jordan. Now therefore take you twelve men out of the tribes of Israel, out of every tribe a man. And it shall come to pass, as soon as the soles of the feet of the priests that bear the ark of the LORD, the LORD of all the earth, shall rest in the waters of Jordan, that the waters of Jordan shall be cut off from the waters that come down from above; and they shall stand upon an heap. And it came to pass, when the people removed from their tents, to pass over Jordan, and the priests bearing the ark of the covenant before the people;

"And as they that bare the ark were come unto Jordan, and the feet of the priests that bare the ark were dipped in the brim of the water, (for Jordan overfloweth all his banks all the time of harvest,) That the waters which came down from above stood and rose up upon an heap very far from the city Adam, that is beside Zaretan: and those that came down toward the sea of the plain, even the salt sea, failed, and were cut off: and the people passed over right against Jericho. **And the priests that bare the ark of the covenant of the LORD stood firm on dry ground in the midst of Jordan**, and all the Israelites passed over on dry ground, until all the people were passed clean over Jordan."

Joshua 3:9–17

God (who here is titled "Lord of all the Earth") supernaturally parted the Jordan River, creating a divine pathway for the Levite priests bearing the Ark of the Covenant to lead the nation across dry ground into the Promised Land. After crossing, Joshua was instructed to perform two rituals – both involving 12 stones. The first was to take 12 stones from the floor of the Jordan River and erect a mound on the shores of Gilgal as a memorial of the great miracle God performed in parting the waters of the Jordan (Joshua 4:1-8).

The 12 stones on the shore represented God's blessing and salvation to those who believe. 1,500 years later, preaching in Bathabarra or the "house of the passage" – the very site where the Israelites crossed Jordan, John the Baptist referenced those very stones:

> "Then went out to him Jerusalem, and all Judaea, and all the region round about Jordan, And were baptized of him in Jordan, confessing their sins. But when he saw many of the Pharisees and Sadducees come to his baptism, he said unto them, O generation of vipers, who hath warned you to flee from the wrath to come? Bring forth therefore fruits meet for repentance: And think not to say within yourselves, We have Abraham to our father: **for I say unto you, that God is able of these stones to raise up children unto Abraham."**
>
> **Matthew 3:5-9**

John the Baptist, the forerunner to the Seed of the Woman, identified those who were of the seed of Satan (the sinful religious leaders of the day) and pointed to the stones commemorating God's Divine proclamation of His sovereignty and salvation. All on the shores of the Jordan River.

At the Tigris river, also known as "Hiddekel" and "the great river" in Scripture (Daniel 10:4, LXX), the prophet Daniel witnessed the appearance of an angel:

"And in the four and twentieth day of the first month, *as I was by the side of the great river*, which is Hiddekel; Then I lifted up mine eyes, and looked, and behold a certain man clothed in linen, whose loins were girded with fine gold of Uphaz: His body also was like the beryl, and his face as the appearance of lightning, and his eyes as lamps of fire, and his arms and his feet like in colour to polished brass, and the voice of his words like the voice of a multitude. And I Daniel alone saw the vision: for the men that were with me saw not the vision; but a great quaking fell upon them, so that they fled to hide themselves."

Daniel 10:1–7

CLOSE ENCOUNTER OF THE DIVINE KIND

The prophet Ezekiel witnessed an appearance of God in a stunning way. At the shore of the river Chebar, The Lord appeared in whirlwind of fire and clouds riding upon a Cherubim:

"Now it came to pass in the thirtieth year, in the fourth month, in the fifth day of the month, as I was among the captives **by the river of Chebar, that the heavens were opened, and I saw visions of God.** In the fifth day of the month, which was the fifth year of king Jehoiachin's captivity, The word of the LORD came expressly unto Ezekiel the priest, the son of Buzi, in the land of the Chaldeans by the river Chebar; and the hand of the LORD was there upon him. And I looked, and, behold, a whirlwind came out of the north, a great cloud, and a fire infolding itself, and a brightness was about it, and out of the midst thereof as the colour of amber, out of the midst of the fire. Also out of the midst thereof came the likeness of four living creatures. And this was their appearance; they had the likeness of a man. And every one had four faces, and every one had four wings. And their feet were straight feet; and the sole of their feet was like the sole of a calf's foot: and they sparkled like the colour of burnished brass."

Ezekiel 1:1–7

The heavens literally opened providing a portal for God to enter the human realm. And once again the divine encounter took place at a river.

ENOCH - A STUNNING PROPHECY LED HIM TO WALK WITH GOD

If there is ever an example of how prophecy can serve as a powerful witness, look no further than the life of Enoch. While this prophet of God is well-known for his great faith and being one of two men in the Bible bestowed with the honor of having "waked with God", it is the timing of Enoch's commitment to holiness that provides profounds revelation:

> "And Enoch lived sixty and five years, and begat Methuselah: **And Enoch walked with God after he begat Methuselah** three hundred years, and begat sons and daughters: And all the days of Enoch were three hundred sixty and five years: And Enoch walked with God: and he was not; for God took him."
>
> **Genesis 5:18–24**

It was not until after the birth of Methuselah that Enoch devoted himself to walking with The Lord. Why? Because in the child's birth God gave Enoch a prophecy of the impending destruction of the Earth. The Hebrew translation of *Methuselah* is: "When he is dead, it shall be sent." Such an ominous title was an indication that Enoch received divine revelation at the birth of Methuselah. And the prophetic message was of a coming judgment upon the earth. A closer look at the timelines of the genealogies of the patriarchs suggests that it is no coincidence that Methuselah died in the same year the Flood was sent upon the earth! Enoch knew centuries in advance that the destruction of the earth and human civilization was linked to the life and death of his child. Theologian A.W. Pink succinctly captured the shock and awe Enoch likely experienced upon receiving this message from the Creator:

> "Suppose God should say to you, *'The life of that little one is to be the life of the world. When that child dies the will be destroyed?'* What would be the effect upon you? Not knowing how soon that child might die, there would come before you the possibility that the world might perish at any time. Every time that child fell sick the world's doom would stare you in the face! Suppose further, that you were unsaved. Would you not

be deeply exercised? Would you not realize as never before your urgent need of preparing to meet God? Would you not at once begin to occupy yourself with spiritual things? May not some such effects have been produced upon Enoch? Be this as it may—and it is difficult to escape such a conclusion it is certainly implied that from the time Methuselah was born, the world lost all its attractiveness for Enoch and from that time on, if never before, he walked with God." – *Gleanings in Genesis*, A. W. Pink, Moody Bible Institute of Chicago, 1922, p. 78

8. Enoch heard God's prophecy and it changed his life forever. How would you have reacted to this news if this was your child? Knowing end times prophecy and what will take place, what are three areas that you can improve in your walk and testimony in these last days? Identify them in a prayer for god to strengthen you

THE FIRST RAPTURE

"By faith Enoch was translated that he should not see death; and was not found, because God had translated him: for before his translation he had this testimony, that he pleased God."

Hebrews 11:5

The rapture of Enoch was one of the greatest events of the ancient world. The first prophet stood for God during a time when his own cousin Lamech was experiencing unprecedent prosperity from secret angelic knowledge. But for everything the fallen angels promised - they could not give humanity eternal life. Enoch proved that through faith, God can. Never let the "successes" of the world distract you from the greatest blessing only Jesus Christ can give - eternal life.

9. What are the similarities between the raptures of Enoch and Elijah?

10. What does Methuselah's lifespan reveal about god?

11. "And the Lord said, _____:
_____ yet
his days shall be an hundred and twenty years." - Genesis 6:3

11. What is the Hebrew translation for "strive" in the verse above? What does this verse say about God's mercy towards us?

12. Explain the significance of the phrase "for that he also is flesh" (Genesis 6:3)

Imagine the world's reaction when Enoch, the prophet of God who spent years pleading with his friends, neighbors, and anyone who would listen that the end of the world was near, was suddenly snatched from Earth to Heaven, soaring through the clouds and never seen again, and leaving behind a son whose death would be the sign that God's wrath was set to be unleashed on an unbelieving society. That rapture served as stunning testimony that the God Enoch spoke of was real, thus giving people more reason to believe and turn back to the Lord.

People knew Enoch was raptured. Hebrews 11 states: "…he was not found." There was a search party sent out to confirm if the First Prophet was truly taken to Heaven. A similar investigation took place at the rapture of the prophet Elijah:

> "And when the sons of the prophets which were to view at Jericho saw
> him, they said, The spirit of Elijah doth rest on Elisha. And they came to
> meet him, and bowed themselves to the ground before him. And they said
> unto him, Behold now, there be with thy servants fifty strong men; let
> them go, we pray thee, and seek thy master: lest peradventure the Spirit of
> the LORD hath taken him up, and cast him upon some mountain, or into
> some valley. And he said, Ye shall not send. And when they urged him till
> he was ashamed, he said, Send. They sent therefore fifty men; and they
> sought three days, **but found him not**. And when they came again to him,
> (for he tarried at Jericho,) he said unto them, Did I not say unto you, Go
> not?"
>
> **2 Kings 2:11–18**

WHEN GOD'S MERCY COMES TO AN END

There is a limit to the amount of unrepentant sin The Lord will allow from a person, nation or era. In the days of Noah, the spiritual and genetic corruption of humanity was so horrific, The Lord announced a time limit for His mercy:

> "And the LORD said, My spirit shall not always strive with man, for that he
> also is flesh: yet his days shall be an hundred and twenty years."
>
> **Genesis 6:3**

The Lord pronounced His judgment on the genetic and moral corruption that occurred at the hands of these sinful angels. Human civilization, overrun with the invasion of the fallen angels and Nephilim, was going to reach a point where God's Spirit would cease to work on its behalf.

"…My spirit shall not always strive with man…"

The word "strive" in Hebrew is *diyn,* which means to "judge, contend or plead." God was not going to allow His Holy Spirit to judge the works of this corrupted pre-Flood world forever. The Lord set a time limit to extend man the opportunity to repent from the rampant wickedness and genetic corruption that was engulfing the world. Genesis 6 provides a chilling description of the spiritual state of humanity:

> "And God saw that the wickedness of man was great in the earth, and that every imagination of the thoughts of his heart was only evil continually."
>
> **Genesis 6:5**

Consider the gravity of this verse. Every thought of every person on the planet was only "evil continually." Unrestrained sinful desires consumed the entire global population as they were contaminated with Nephilim genetics. Noah, who was a "preacher of righteousness" proclaimed God's Word and constructed the ark for over a century. And not one person heeded the call to repentance and safety except for his sons and their wives.

"... for that he also is flesh..." – Unlocking a Mysterious Phrase

> "And the LORD said, My spirit shall not always strive with man, **for that he also is flesh**: yet his days shall be an hundred and twenty years."
>
> **Genesis 6:3**

Oftentimes a small verse holds a great deal of information. As God prepared to judge the world, He noted that man "also is flesh." Bible commentator Watchman Nee provides insight into the meaning of this pronouncement:

"The passage in Genesis 6.3 is clear: 'for that he [man] also is flesh.' What is meant here by the word 'also'? It means the second time. For instance, You have eaten, but I also have eaten. This 'also' means the second time. God says that man also is flesh, indicating that before man somebody else has first become flesh. Who, aside from man, can be spoken in such parallel fashion to man? **None but the angel. Hence in saying that man also is flesh, it implies that the angels had already become flesh.** With such evidence as this, we can assuredly conclude that 'the sons of God' points to the angels."
— *How to Study the Bible: Practical Advice for Receiving Light from God's Word*, Watchman Nee, Living Stream Ministry, p. 130. [emphasis added]

EXPERIENCE GOD

13. Complete the verses which describe attributes of God you saw in chapters 5 and 6

GOD WILL JUDGE ALL SIN

"Behold, the Lord cometh with ten thousands of his saints, To_____

_____

_____." — Jude 1:14

THE PORTAL BETWEEN HEAVEN AND EARTH

"...and, lo, the heavens were opened unto him, and he saw_____

_____" - Matthew 3:16-17

GOD'S WARNING

"And Enoch lived sixty and five years, and begat Methuselah: And Enoch walked with God_____

_____

_____" — Genesis 5:21-22

WALKING IN FAITH

"O man, what is good; and what doth the LORD require of thee, but

_____?" " - Micah 6:7

14. What role do these attributes play in your walk with God?

4.   BIRTH OF THE NEPHILIM

CHAPTERS 7-8

How could an angel conceive a child with a human woman? This is one of the most challenging questions in Christian theology. But the fact is the Bible very clearly details giants existing and thus it must explain their origin.

KEY THEMES:

- There was serious angelic rebellion against God in ancient times. And it takes deep Bible study to reveal this history.
- By letting Scripture interpret Scripture, the Bible provides an explanation for the human-angelic relations leading to the birth of the Nephilim.
- The flood was a necessary judgment of God to cleanse the world of the genetic contamination that threatened to exterminate humanity.
- This has been the common understanding in the Church for millennia.

1. What is the Greek translation of "habitation" in Jude 1:6-7? Why does it matter for this study?

2. What do Jude 1:6-7 and the Genesis 18 account of Sodom and Gomorrah tell us about the sin of the Genesis 6 apostate angels?

3. How does Job 4:17-18 describe the sins of the fallen angels?

4. Give three examples from Scripture of the use of the word "folly" that demonstrate contextually that it refers to fornication?

DID ANGELS REALLY MARRY HUMAN WOMEN?

It seems bizarre, confusing and even impossible to some, but the Bible clearly teaches that the sin of the Genesis 6 apostate angels was that of fornication. Jude 1:6-7 informs us that they "left their first estate" – serving God in righteousness in the heavenly realm - to "go after strange flesh" – namely that of human women.

In committing this iniquity, they also defiled their bodies. The Greek term for "habitation" - *oikētērion* - occurs only twice in the Bible. The only other instance is in 2 Corinthians 5:

> "For we know that if our earthly house of this tabernacle were dissolved, we have a building of God, an house not made with hands, eternal in the

heavens. For in this we groan, earnestly desiring to be clothed upon with our house (oikētērion) which is from heaven: If so be that being clothed we shall not be found naked. For we that are in this tabernacle do groan, being burdened: not for that we would be unclothed, but clothed upon, that mortality might be swallowed up of life. Now he that hath wrought us for the selfsame thing is God, who also hath given unto us the earnest of the Spirit. Therefore we are always confident, knowing that, whilst we are at home in the body, we are absent from the Lord."

2 Corinthians 5:1–6

The Greek word *oikētērion* is used here metaphorically to describe the glorified, heavenly body a born-again believer will eventually receive as a "house" that believers "earnestly" desire to be clothed with. The Apostle Paul, under the Holy Spirit's inspiration, explains that for Christians the flesh bodies we are born with pale in comparison to the heavenly bodies we will receive at the Rapture when all believers are translated. This celestial body is immortal and does not contain the sin nature that all human beings have inherited from Adam. So, the "house" that Paul desires is the same "habitation", or *oikētērion,* that the angels who sinned chose to desecrate to pursue their sinful schemes. These fallen angels succumbed to evil desires, degraded their habitation in an immortal, heavenly body, and became "flesh" – stained with sin and destined for God's judgment.

Jude compares this sin to Sodom and Gomorrah, an incident where humans attempted to fornicate with angels:

"And there came two angels to Sodom at even; and Lot sat in the gate of Sodom: and Lot seeing them rose up to meet them; and he bowed himself with his face toward the ground; And he said, Behold now, my lords, turn in, I pray you, into your servant's house, and tarry all night, and wash your feet, and ye shall rise up early, and go on your ways. And they said, Nay; but we will abide in the street all night. And he pressed upon them greatly; and they turned in unto him, and entered into his house; and he made them a feast, and did bake unleavened bread, and they did eat. But before they lay down, the men of the city, even the men of Sodom, compassed the house round, both old and young, all the people from every quarter: And they called unto Lot, and said unto him, Where are the men which came in to thee this night? bring them out unto us, that we may know them. And Lot went out at the door unto them, and shut the door after him, And said, I pray you, brethren, do not so wickedly."

Genesis 19:1–7

Count this as another passage that the church teaches but often omits the supernatural narrative taking place. This was not merely an attempt at homosexual assault, it was a potential return to the sins of Genesis 6. And it was so grievous The Lord came down to personally investigate the sins of these two cities. As was the case in so many instances in Scripture, any sin involving the Nephilim or fallen angelic-human relations resulted in swift, devastating judgment from Yahweh. Sodom and Gomorrah suffered the judgment of fire and brimstone – something the apostle Jude made a direct connection:

"And the angels which kept not their first estate, but left their own habitation, he hath reserved in everlasting chains under darkness unto the judgment of the great day. Even as Sodom and Gomorrah, and the cities about them in like manner, giving themselves over to fornication, and going after strange flesh, are set forth for an example, suffering the vengeance of eternal fire."

Jude 1:6-7

THE SIN OF "FOLLY"

"Behold, he put no trust in his servants; and his angels he charged with folly:"

Job 4:18

This verse is not often connected to the Nephilim but upon close examination, it is further proof that what took place in the Days of Noah was indeed sexual sin. Though folly normally refers to silly behavior, contextually it is used in Scripture to refer to sexual sin:

"And Dinah the daughter of Leah, which she bare unto Jacob, went out to see the daughters of the land. And when Shechem the son of Hamor the Hivite, prince of the country, saw her, he took her, and lay with her, and defiled her... And the sons of Jacob came out of the field when they heard it: and the men were grieved, and they were very wroth, **because he had wrought folly in Israel in lying with Jacob's daughter: which thing ought not to be done**."

Genesis 34:1–2, 7

"And it came to pass after this, that Absalom the son of David had a fair sister, whose name was Tamar; and Amnon the son of David loved her. And Amnon was so vexed, that he fell sick for his sister Tamar; for she was a virgin; and Amnon thought it hard for him to do anything to her... And when she had brought them unto him to eat, he took hold of her, and said unto her, Come lie with me, my sister. And she answered him, Nay, my brother, do not force me; for no such thing ought to be done in Israel: do not thou this folly."

2 Samuel 13:1–2; 11–12

All these passages involve horrific and criminal acts of fornication. So when Job chapter 4 reveals that The Lord charges the angels with "folly", it is further evidence of the Genesis 6 supernatural interpretation. Charles Leslie, writing in 1702, agreed with this conclusion:

"He tells us of their Fall: *Behold he put no trust in his Servants and his Angels he charged with folly,* Job iv.8. Again, *Behold he putteth no trust in his Saints Yea the Heavens are not clean in his sight* Job xv.15. This uncleanness in the Inhabitants of Heaven seems rather to allude to this Fall of the Angels by Incontinency, than that of Pride and Ambition. And I do not know why it may not intimate their polluting of the Holy Seed." – *A Sermon Preach'd at Chester: Against Marriages in Different Communion*, Charles Leslie, Henry Dodwell, 1702, p. 165.

Provide a Bible verse and explanation of the following:

4. Angels have physical bodies

5. Angels can physically interact with human beings

6. Angels have a similar physiology to humans

7. Using 1 Corinthians 15 and at least 3 supporting verses, provide a Biblical explanation as to how the conception of the Nephilim was possible.

HOW IS IT POSSIBLE?

One of the most challenging questions of this study: how was it possible for a human woman to conceive a child with an angel? Fortunately, the Bible provides enough evidence to explain. It begins with understanding that angels have a physical presence.

- ANGELS HAVE BODIES

  When Jesus, accompanied by 2 angels, visited Abraham's home in Genesis 18, it was clear that they had physical bodies. In the chapter, Abraham, recognizing that it was God and 2 of His host, graciously stated: **Let a little water, I pray you, be fetched, and wash your feet, and rest yourselves under the tree**: And I will fetch a morsel of bread, and comfort ye your hearts;" (Genesis 18:4-5). And once the distinguished divine guests agreed to stay, their meal was prepared:

  "And Abraham ran unto the herd, and fetch a calf tender and good, and gave it unto a young man; and he hasted to dress it. And he took butter, and milk, and the calf which he had dressed, and set it before them; and he stood by them under the tree, and they did eat."
  Genesis 18:7-8

  Jesus and the two angels had their feet washed, ate a meal and rested under a tree. They certainly had physical bodies.

- ANGELS AND HUMANS HAVE A SIMILAR PHYSIOLOGY

As demonstrated in the passage above, angels can eat human food. Conversely, when the Israelites wandered the wilderness during the 40-year judgment, they ate food prepared for angels:

"And had rained down manna upon them to eat, and had given them of the corn of heaven. Man did eat angels' food: he sent them meat to the full."

Psalm 78:24–25

The manna sent from Heaven was food normally eaten by angels, thus proving that humans and angels have a similar physiology as they can eat each other's food. This should not be as surprising when we remember that God made humanity just "a little lower than the angels." Though we may be inferior, we are not that far off from the heavenly host.

- ANGELS CAN PHYSICALLY INTERACT WITH HUMAN BEINGS

The prophet Daniel met the angel Gabriel and was overwhelmed by the appearance of the angels. So much so he fell unconscious. The angel soon picked him up off the ground:

"So he came near where I stood: and when he came, I was afraid, and fell upon my face: but he said unto me, Understand, O son of man: for at the time of the end shall be the vision. Now as he was speaking with me, I was in a deep sleep on my face toward the ground: but he touched me, and set me upright."

Daniel 8:15–18

- ANGELS HAVE SEED

"But some man will say, How are the dead raised up? and with what body do they come? Thou fool, that which thou sowest is not quickened, except it die: And that which thou sowest, thou sowest not that body that shall be, but bare grain, it may chance of wheat, or of some other grain: **But God gives it a body as it hath pleased him, and to every seed his own body.** All flesh is not the same flesh: but there is one kind of flesh of men, another flesh of beasts, another of fishes, and another of birds. There are also celestial bodies, and bodies terrestrial: but the glory of the celestial is one, and the glory of the terrestrial is another."

1 Corinthians 15:36–40

1 Corinthians 15 is one of the most amazing chapters of Scripture. The Apostle Paul explains several complex concepts in this one section of the Bible. Among them is the passage above where he contrasts the "celestial body" – the immortal, heavenly body angels possess (and that born-again Christians will receive at the Rapture) – and the "terrestrial body" the earthly, mortal body we are born with. And in this comparison Paul revealed every creature that The Lord has given a body to also receives "seed." In the Biblical context this is a reference to the genetic material needed to reproduce.

Thus, the angels, who we have established, possess bodies, **also have seed**. Combining this information with the fact that angels have physical bodies, can physically interact with humans, can resemble human beings and have a similar physiology, the notion that a human woman could conceive a hybrid offspring with a fallen angel, takes on a great deal more feasibility. Adding the testimony of Genesis 6 (the sons of God took wives of which all they chose"), Jude (the angels went after strange flesh) and Job 4 (the angels were charged with folly) – the full picture of what took place in the days of Noah is revealed.

Thomas Stokes, a theologian writing in the 19th century, confirmed this interpretation:

> "All flesh is not the same flesh, (1 Cor. xv. 39). The next verse informs us that there is celestial as well as terrestrial flesh. Several instances of celestial flesh we have recorded. The angels who visited Abraham and partook of his fare; (Gen. xviii. 2, 8), and two of them pulled Lot in, and took hold of his hand, (xix. 10, 16). The angel also that wrestled with Jacob, (xxxii. 24, 30), **and the sons of God who begat the giants of the daughters of men**, (vi. 2. Jude 6), This appears to be the origin of the heathen mythology of the ancients. These were the angels that shouted for joy at the creation, before Adam was made, (Job xxxviii. 7), and amongst whom Satan appeared before God, (i. 6, ii. 1). They subsist upon substantial food like us, (Ps lxxviii. 25) and, we are only made a little lower than them, (Heb ii. 7)." – *The Wisdom of*

God Shown Forth by the Opening of the Books, Thomas Stokes, Printed by J. Barker, Wortley, 1847, p. 67.

THE BIRTH OF THE GIANTS

"and they bare children to them, the same became mighty men which were of old, men of renown."

Genesis 6:4

8. Explain Dr. Michael Heiser's and Francois Lenormant's explanation of the etymology of the word "Nephilim"

9. What is the significance of Noah being "perfect in his generations" (Genesis 6:8-9)?

10. What made the Nephilim so evil? Provide a verse and explanation

11. How does the notion of Jesus Christ being "the only begotten Son of God" change in light of the Biblical understanding of sin and genetics?

12. What is the connection between the Nephilim and ancient mythology?

THE RISE OF THE NEPHILIM

The sin of Genesis 6 led to the birth of the Nephilim. Rather than meaning "tyrants" or "bully" or a similar term, the Hebrew word Nephilim means "giant." Dr. Michael Heiser provides the most sound explanation of the etymology of the word Nephilim:

> "The only way in Hebrew to get *Nephilim* from *naphal* by the rules of Hebrew morphology (word formation) would be to presume a noun spelled *naphil* and then pluralize it.

> "I say 'presume' since this noun does not exist in biblical Hebrew — unless one counts Genesis 6:4 and Numbers 13:33, the two occurrences of *Nephilim* — but that would then be assuming what one is trying to prove! However, in Aramaic the noun naphil(a) does exist. It means 'giant,' making it easy to see why the Septuagint (the ancient Greek translation of the Hebrew Bible) translated *Nephilim* as *gigantes* ('giant') .... It is most likely that *Nephilim* is an Aramaic term imported into Hebrew during the final editing of the Hebrew Bible in Babylon (where Aramaic was the lingua franca) and then the ending was corrected to Hebrew rules of word formation. Both phenomena are known in the Hebrew Bible." — Michael Heiser, http://www.sitchiniswrong.com/Nephilim/Nephilim.htm

Nephilim is derived from the Aramaic word *Naphil*, which means "giant." Archaeologist and historian Francois Lenormant agreed with this understanding. Of note also is that in the

Septuagint, the oldest extant version of the Old Testament, the term *gigantes* is used to refer to the Nephilim, which again means "giant."

The Nephilim dominated antediluvian society with violence. They were mighty warriors with superhuman strength who brought corruption and sin to into human genetics. Their contamination was so widespread Noah was likely the last of the fully human believers left on earth:

> "But Noah found grace in the eyes of the LORD. These are the generations
> of Noah: Noah was a just man **and perfect in his generations**, and Noah
> walked with God." **Genesis 6:8–9**

Noah was chosen to restart humanity after the Flood because he was a believer in God. He was also "perfect in his generations" – part of a genetic ancestry that was 100% human. Noah's lineage was not corrupted by the Nephilim hybridization plaguing humanity. The Hebrew word for "perfect" in Genesis 6:9 is *tamiym*, which means "complete, whole" regarding health and physical condition. This is the same word used to prescribe the condition of animals sacrificed to the Lord:

> "And whosoever offereth a sacrifice of peace offerings unto the LORD to
> accomplish his vow, or a freewill offering in beeves or sheep, it shall be
> perfect (*tamiym*) to be accepted; there shall be no blemish therein." –
> Leviticus 22:21

WHAT MADE THE NEPHILIM SO EVIL?

> "Wherefore, as by one man sin entered into the world, and death by sin;
> and so death passed upon all men, for that all have sinned...."
> **Romans 5:12**

All people are born with a sin nature, which is a corrupted spirit that seeks to fulfill fleshly lusts and sin against God. This is the reason the Bible boldly proclaims "all have sinned." Notice in the verse above that death – the by-product of sin – was "passed upon all men."

Children inherit their spiritual nature from their parents, specifically their fathers. This process is referred to as "begetting" in the Bible.

For the Nephilim, they received the hyper-depraved sin nature of their fallen angelic fathers, accelerating their wickedness. Even many generations removed from the original giants, the Nephilim Goliath still displayed their same arrogance, wickedness and antagonism towards God's people:

> "And he [Goliath] stood and cried unto the armies of Israel, and said unto them, Why are ye come out to set your battle in array? am not I a Philistine, and ye servants to Saul? choose you a man for you, and let him come down to me. If he be able to fight with me, and to kill me, then will we be your servants: but if I prevail against him, and kill him, then shall ye be our servants, and serve us. And the Philistine said, I defy the armies of Israel this day; give me a man, that we may fight together."
> **1 Samuel 17:8–10**

The "champion [*gibborim* in Hebrew] of the Philistines" was the only Nephilim in ancient Biblical history whose spoken words are recorded. And his entire presentation displayed his defiance of God and desire to kill or rule over the Israelites. He demanded a fight to the death to make the entire nation his slaves. This gives insight into the sinful spirit of the giants. It stands to reasons that Goliath's ancestors, the original Nephilim who were born directly from the fallen angels, were not only larger in stature, but even more wicked.

The original giants were the "gods" of ancient heathen mythology. Scripture supports this by calling them "men of renown." Hercules, Achilles, and other demi-gods of mythology were all based on the history of Genesis 6. Robert Purdon captured how influential they were in antiquity:

> "Those men with angelic blood in their veins became the leaders and rulers of mankind. The fire, the genius, the beauty, the strength and the strong will

descended from birth to birth from the ancestral Angels to their earth born posterity." – *The Last Vials: Being a Series of Essays on the Second Advent*, No. X, 22nd year, Sept. 1st, 1867, Robert Purdon, p. 6.

THE ONLY BEGOTTEN SON

Because of the sin nature passing from fathers to their children, it was ultimately necessary for the Messiah to avoid inheriting this corrupted nature that started with Adam. This is why Jesus was born of Mary but was begotten by God The Father – thus His spiritual nature was wholly Divine and without sin. In salvation, Jesus can pass on His perfect, righteous spiritual nature to all who believe upon His name for the forgiveness of their sins. Therefore it is of paramount import that Christ was the *only begotten* Son of God. In this unique position, He stands as the only person in the universe born with the perfect, righteous Holy Spirit of God in Him. "For in him dwelleth all the fulness of the Godhead bodily" (Colossians 2:9).

Citing an ancient scholar or text provide supporting evidence for each point below regarding the Nephilim

14. They were famous for their size

15. They defied God

16. God destroyed them for their evil

5.   THE END OF THE WORLD

CHAPTER 9-10

Noah lived for 120 years knowing the world was going to be destroyed by a cataclysmic flood judgment from God. The Flood was a foreshadow of the end times judgment of Revelation and of the Kingdom of Christ to come.

KEY THEMES:

- Noah redeemed the time by living in obedience to The Lord and preaching righteousness to a world full of non-believers. He never gave up on his mission.
- After the Garden of Eden, the ark was the second supernaturally designed structure in the Bible.
- The judgment of the Nephilim was so legendary in ancient times, that the Rephaim became synonymous with the dead in Jewish culture.

"But in the ark the Lord provided hope. Like the Garden of Eden, the ark was designed by God. It served as a temporary temple and picture of God's salvation for those who believe. " – *Judgment Of The Nephilim*

1. List 3 similarities between the Ark and the Tabernacle or Temples of God in the Bible (include verse references)

2. What was William Henry Pinnock's understanding of Genesis 2:5-6?

3. Provide and explain 2 examples of the Bible using floods as a metaphor (Include Scripture reference)

4. What are common perceptions of non-believers when it comes to God and the flood judgment?

5. How can you explain God's Purpose in sending the Flood in light of Genesis 6?

THE ARK – A TEMPLE ON THE WATER

After the Garden of Eden, the ark was the second Divinely designed structure on earth. The specific dimensions and instructions for its construction were given to Noah directly from God. And during a time of judgment, the vessel served as both salvation for faithful Noah and a temple. Consider some of the similarities between the dimensions of the ark and the tabernacle and temples of God:

- The precise dimensions of the ark, the tabernacle, Solomon's temple, and the Millennial temple were all given by God.
- The length of the ark was 300 cubits (Genesis 6:15). The length of the inner court of Ezekiel's Millennial temple is 300 cubits (Ezekiel 40:23, 27, 47).
- The height of the ark was 30 cubits. The inner temple of the most holy place in Solomon's temple, where the Ark of the Covenant was kept, was 30 cubits in height (1 Kings 6:2).
- The Lord instructed Noah "… rooms shalt thou make in the ark" (Genesis 6:14). Both the temple of Solomon and the Millennial temple had side rooms as part of their design (1 Kings 6:8, Ezekiel 41:16).
- The ark was three stories high. The temple of Solomon and the Millennial temple are three stories high (1 Kings 6:8, Ezekiel 41:16).
- The ark's design provided for a window at the top of the vessel. The temple of Solomon had windows on its ceiling of "narrow light" (1 Kings 6:4).

The ark was a picture of the Lord's salvation in the midst of the judgment of the ungodly. While the waves crashed, millions perished, and whole cities sank to the ocean floor, Noah and his family rested safely in the ark.

THE FLOOD – THE FIRST APOCALYPSE

Imagine a cataclysm that wiped out every structure on Earth and destroyed 99% of the human population. Though the planet was still standing, for all intents and purposes, the flood was the end of the world for the ancients. The shock it must have been to the antediluvians once the first rain drops fell from the sky. William Henry Pinnock, a 19th century clergyman, understood that based on Genesis 2:5-6, it never rained before the flood. The vegetation of the earth received its water from mist that emanated from the soil:

> "And every plant of the field before it was in the earth, and every herb of the field before it grew: for the LORD God had not caused it to rain upon the earth, and there was not a man to till the ground. But there went up a mist from the earth, and watered the whole face of the ground"
> **Genesis 2:5–6**

Throughout the Old Testament, the Flood was so legendary, it was used as a metaphor for any tribulation someone experienced:

> "The sorrows of death compassed me, and the floods of ungodly men made me afraid."
> **Psalm 18:4**

> "And with the arms of a flood shall they be overflown from before him, and shall be broken; yea, also the prince of the covenant."
> **Daniel 11:22**

"HOW COULD A LOVING GOD FLOOD THE WORLD?"

One of the most important aspects of the supernatural interpretation of Genesis 6 is that it provides an answer to one of the most challenging questions posed to the Bible: how could a loving God send a flood judgment that destroyed 99% of the human population? When you understand that what was taking place in the antediluvian world was an attempt to destroy the human race by corrupting human genetics and erasing any chance of salvation for mankind, then rather than being the irrational punishment of the "angry God of the Old Testament" – the flood was a rescue. The Devil was so close in his attack, that Noah and his sons were the last purely human believer left on Earth.

By putting Noah and his family on the ark and unleashing the flood, The Lord was cleansing the Earth of the Nephilim and their genetic contamination, punishing the fallen angels who committed the sin of fornication and providing humanity with a new start to be fruitful and multiply. And it preserved the Messianic lineage. The judgment of the Nephilim and the angels who sinned was an act of love, pulling humanity back from the brink of utter destruction and catastrophe. Being able to explain the account of Genesis 6 provides an answer to one of the biggest stumbling blocks to unbelievers.

SHEOL – ABODE OF THE DEAD

6. What does the story of the Rich man and the beggar Lazarus tell us about *Sheol* before the first coming of Christ?

7. What is an example from King David's writings that confirms this understanding of Sheol?

8. What was Reverend Samuel Barnum's interpretation of the use of *"rapha"* in connection to Sheol?

9. Citing an ancient scholar, provide an explanation of how the Nephilim became associated with Sheol

A PLACE FOR THE RIGHTEOUS AND SINNERS

In Old Testament times, all people who died went to Sheol, or the grave. What we commonly call "Hell" was actually an abode for the spirits of the deceased with multiple compartments. The clearest explanation of this was provided by The Lord Jesus Christ in the account of the Rich Man and the beggar Lazarus. In this account, both men die and their spirits go to Sheol. However, when they arrive, Lazarus, who had faith in God, is resting in comfort in area known as "Abraham's bosom" – signifying it is reserved for those who like Abraham, had faith in Messiah which was "accounted to them for righteousness." (Genesis 15:6).

The Rich Man, conversely, found himself burning in fire in an area called "torments." Abraham explained to the man (who clearly died without repentance or faith) that there was a large "gulf" separating them which the Rich Man could not cross. There are many powerful spiritual lessons in this account but for the purposes of this study we note that prior to the crucifixion of Christ, all people went to Sheol at death.

King David made reference to this when he wrote:

> "I will praise thee, O Lord my God, with all my heart: and I will glorify thy
> name for evermore. For great is thy mercy toward me: and thou hast
> delivered my soul from the lowest hell [*Sheol*]."
> **Psalm 86:12–13**

THE GIANTS BECAME ASSOCIATED WITH THE DEAD

Because the memory of the flood resonated so strongly with ancient near eastern culture, the giants, who were also called Rephaim, became associated with "the dead." So much so, that the word for "dead" in Hebrew is *rapha*, the singular form of Rephaim.

> "It is joy to the just to do judgment: but destruction shall be to the workers
> of iniquity. The man that wandereth out of the way of understanding shall
> remain in the congregation of the dead [*rapha*]."
> **Proverbs 21:15–16**

Reverend Samuel Barnum remarked on this development:

> "An attentive consideration seems to leave little room for doubt that the
> dead were called Rephaim, from some notion of *Sheol* (A.V. 'hell') being the
> residence of the fallen spirits or buried giants." – *A Comprehensive Dictionary
> of the Bible*, Mainly Abridged from WM. Smith's Dictionary of The Bible,
> edited by Rev. Samuel W. Barnum, 1888, p. 333.

Theologian Charles Peters, writing in 1757, added more detail to the explanation:

> "For this was properly the place of the *rephaim*; the word originally denoting
> those giants in impiety, that were overwhelmed by the flood; and from
> thence it came afterwards to [signify] the names of wicked men, or men of
> violence like them, who as they died, were gathered to their [assembly]." –

A Critical Dissertation on the Book of Job, The Second Edition – corrected, Charles Peters, 1757, p. 360.

All of this serves as another example of how the account of the Nephilim weaves its way throughout the entire Old Testament (and into the New Testament as well).

6.   THE RISE AND FALL OF THE ASSYRIAN

CHAPTERS 11 AND 12

Ezekiel 31 and 32 are some of the most mysterious chapters in Scripture. They detail the rise and fall of the Assyrian - the angel who ruled the antediluvian world of fallen Sons of God and their Nephilim offspring.

KEY THEMES:

- **The Assyrian is not Satan.** They are different angels.
- When God unleashed the flood judgment, the Assyrian and the angels who took human wives were dragged down to the abyss where they were put in chains under darkness.
- Ezekiel 31 provides more references to the Garden of Eden than any other chapter in Scripture.
- Understanding these chapters provides amazing insight and detail into the specific reasoning and timing of the of the judgment of the angels who sinned.

THE RISE AND FALL OF THE ASSYRIAN

Ezekiel 31 and 32 chronicle the rise and fall of the supreme angel who ruled the antediluvian kingdom of fallen angels and their Nephilim children. This king, referred to as "the Assyrian," was the first global ruler and the most powerful of all the Genesis 6 apostate angels. The book of Ezekiel chronicles his rise to prominence, the destruction of his kingdom, and one of the main reasons the Lord administered such a catastrophic flood judgment.

Ezekiel 31 is an "esoteric passage" – a chapter or portion of Scripture where The Lord makes a pronouncement to a king or prince but in reality, His message is directed at a fallen angel. By far the most commonly known example of this is found in Isaiah 14:

> "That thou shalt take up this proverb against the king of Babylon, and say, How hath the oppressor ceased! …How art thou fallen from heaven, O Lucifer, son of the morning! how art thou cut down to the ground, which didst weaken the nations! For thou hast said in thine heart, I will ascend into heaven, I will exalt my throne above the stars of God: I will sit also upon the mount of the congregation, in the sides of the north: I will ascend above the heights of the clouds; I will be like the most High."
>
> **Isaiah 14:4; 11–14**

Though addressed to "the king of Babylon" this passage details the aspirations of Satan. Exalting his throne "above the stars of God", ascending into Heaven and sitting above the heights of the clouds are all Scriptural indicators that an angelic being is in view. A similar address is found in Ezekiel 28, which provides a glimpse into the history of Satan before his initial sinful rebellion:

> "Son of man, take up a lamentation upon the king of Tyrus, and say unto him, Thus saith the Lord GOD; Thou sealest up the sum, full of wisdom, and perfect in beauty. **Thou hast been in Eden the garden of God;**

every precious stone was thy covering, the sardius, topaz, and the diamond, the beryl, the onyx, and the jasper, the sapphire, the emerald, and the carbuncle, and gold: the workmanship of thy tabrets and of thy pipes was prepared in thee in the day that thou wast created. **Thou art the anointed cherub that covereth; and I have set thee so: thou wast upon the holy mountain of God; thou hast walked up and down in the midst of the stones of fire**. Thou wast perfect in thy ways from the day that thou wast created, till iniquity was found in thee."

Ezekiel 28:12-15

Ezekiel 31 is *also* an esoteric passage but it is addressed to the fallen angel who led the Genesis 6 rebels in taking human women as wives, fathering the Nephilim and ruling the preflood world. He is known in the passage as the Assyrian. **<u>This evil angel is not Satan</u>**. This is a different fallen angel that is rarely discussed, taught or even mentioned in any church or seminary. The chapter chronicles his rise to power as the ruler of the fallen angelic-Nephilim hybrid empire and then his fall when Yahweh punished him.

1. Who was the Assyrian? What was his role in the Antediluvian World?

2. Examining Daniel 4 and Amos 2, how can we understand the meaning behind the "tree symbolism" of Ezekiel 31?

3. What was the primary sin God charged the Assyrian with? How does the language of Ezekiel 31 confirm that an angelic being in the antediluvian world is in view?

FALLEN ANGELIC KING OF THE PREFLOOD WORLD

Although Ezekiel 31 appears to be referring to "Pharaoh of Egypt," it is truly directed to the apostate angel who reigned over all the fallen sons of God and Nephilim before the Flood:

> "And it came to pass in the eleventh year, in the third month, in the
> first day of the month, that the word of the LORD came unto me, saying,
> Son of man, speak unto Pharaoh king of Egypt, and to his multitude;
> Whom art thou like in thy greatness? **Behold, the Assyrian was a cedar
> in Lebanon with fair branches, and with a shadowing shroud, and of
> an high stature**; and his top was among the thick boughs."
> Ezekiel 31:1–3

Some Bible students will recognize parallels between this passage and the other, more popular esoteric Scriptures. "Pharaoh" or "the Assyrian" was incomparable in his level of "greatness." A similar lofty compliment is given at the beginning of Isaiah 14 and Ezekiel 28. The Assyrian was a "cedar in Lebanon with fair branches." The Lebanese cedar is an extremely tall tree that reaches heights of 130 feet. There is rich biblical imagery in this passage as well. The cedar tree is frequently used in Scripture as a metaphor for mighty beings.

Daniel 4 serves as a "Rosetta Stone" to decipher the complex imagery and metaphoric language of Ezekiel 31. In that chapter, Nebuchadnezzar, King of Babylon, has a dream of a tree that is described in an eerily similar fashion to Ezekiel 31:

> "Thus were the visions of mine head in my bed; I saw, and behold a tree in the
> midst of the earth, and the height thereof was great. The tree grew, and was
> strong, and the height thereof reached unto heaven, and the sight thereof to the

end of all the earth: The leaves thereof were fair, and the fruit thereof much, and in it was meat for all: the beasts of the field had shadow under it, and the fowls of the heaven dwelt in the boughs thereof, and all flesh was fed of it."

Daniel 4:10-12

The language consistency is no coincidence. This is why allowing Scripture to interpret Scripture is such a critical aspect of Bible study. Nebuchadnezzar, a wicked global emperor had the dream of this mighty tree only to find out that the tree in his dream was symbolic of him:

"The tree that thou sawest, which grew, and was strong, whose height reached unto the heaven, and the sight thereof to all the earth; Whose leaves were fair, and the fruit thereof much, and in it was meat for all; under which the beasts of the field dwelt, and upon whose branches the fowls of the heaven had their habitation: **It is thou, O king**, that art grown and become strong: for thy greatness is grown, and reacheth unto heaven, and thy dominion to the end of the earth."

Daniel 4:20-22

Thus the Biblical precedent for a massive tree symbolizing a king is established. Another connection to the Days of Noah is found in Amos 2. In this chapter, The Lord recounts leading the Israelites to victory over the Nephilim Kings Og and Sihon and references cedar trees:

"Yet destroyed I the Amorite before them, whose height was like the height of the cedars, and he was strong as the oaks; yet I destroyed his fruit from above, and his roots from beneath."

Amos 2:9

PRIDE GOETH BEFORE DESTRUCTION

"Thus was he fair in his greatness, in the length of his branches: for his root was by great waters. The cedars in the garden of God could not hide him: the fir trees were not like his boughs, and the chestnut trees were not like his branches; nor any tree in the garden of God was like unto him in his beauty. I have made him fair by the multitude of his branches: so that all the trees of Eden, that were in the garden of God, envied him. Therefore thus saith the Lord GOD; Because thou hast lifted up thyself in height, and he hath shot up his top among the thick boughs, and his heart is lifted up in his height;"

Ezekiel 31:7-10

The above passage details the principal sin of this fallen angelic king: pride. Being the most powerful of the Genesis 6 apostate angels, the other Genesis 6 rebels were jealous of him. The chapter confirms that: "all the trees of Eden, which were in the garden of God, envied him." And in this detail, we receive confirmation that that fallen angels are in view. The Assyrian and the other "trees" were in the Garden of Eden; therefore this could not be a reference to a mortal human king and certainly could not have taken place during Ezekiel's lifetime (when the Garden had been gone for millennia). Ezekiel 31 makes more refences to the Garden of Eden than any other chapter in the Bible.

The Assyrian usurped control of the Garden of Eden and dominated control over of the sin-plagued earth. His "beauty" (a reference to his angelic power) corrupted him and "lifted his heart" with pride – the same iniquity Satan fell into when he was in the Garden of Eden:

"Thine heart was lifted up because of thy beauty. Thou hast corrupted thy wisdom by reason of thy brightness..."

Ezekiel 28:17

4. What was Rev. John Fleming's view on the purpose of the flood? how do we see this in Ezekiel 31:14? How does this affect your view of the Bible and God?

5. Using Ezekiel 31:14-18 and Genesis 8:1-3 explain the timing of the Assyrian's punishment and its connection to the "locusts" of Revelation 9:1-11?

Having overrun the world with his Nephilim hybrid offspring and rebel angel loyalists, the Assyrian threatened to overturn the very plan of salvation The Lord proclaimed from the foundation of the world. And this arrogant aspiration led to his destruction. The incursion of the Sons of God and their corruption of human genetics was the cause of the flood judgment. The Flood's primary purpose was to be the ultimate deterrent to the angelic realm to never attempt fornication with human women again. John Fleming, author of one of the most comprehensive studies on the Nephilim, concurred:

> "An insuperable objection appears to lie against the notion that demon intercourse of the kind in question was carried on subsequently to the Deluge. The purpose of God in bringing on the world that widespread destruction was, we believe, not merely to punish transgressors **but quite as much or more to put a period to the unnatural intercourse of angels with daughters of men,** to prevent the further commingling of different classes of creatures, to obliterate all traces of such intercourse and to exterminate the monstrous offspring to which it had given rise." – *The Fallen Angels and the Heroes of Mythology*, Rev. John Fleming A.B., Dublin: Hodges, Foster, & Figgis, 1879, pp. 108–109.

THE TIMING OF THE ASSYRIAN'S DESTRUCTION AND THE MYSTERIOUS CONECTION TO END TIMES BIBLE PROPHECY

Ezekiel 31 also provides *the timing of the destruction of the Assyrian's kingdom:*

> "Thus saith the Lord GOD; **In the day when he went down to the grave** I caused a mourning: I covered the deep for him, **and I restrained the floods thereof, and the great waters were stayed:** and I caused Lebanon to mourn for him, and all the trees of the field fainted for him."
>
> **Ezekiel 31:15**

After day 150 of the Flood, the waters finally started to "abate":

> "And God remembered Noah, and every living thing, and all the cattle that was with him in the ark: and God made a wind to pass over the earth, and the waters assuaged; The fountains also of the deep and the windows of heaven were stopped, and the rain from heaven was restrained; And the waters returned from off the earth continually: **and after the end of the hundred and fifty days the waters were abated.**"
>
> **Genesis 8:1–3**

Both passages point to the same time in the Flood, the moment God "restrained" or stopped the rain showers from above and "stayed" the massive subterranean waters shooting up from "the deep." The divine force pushing water through the earth's surface ceased and the waters of the deep returned to beneath the earth's crust. The Assyrian was forced to fight for his survival in his ruined kingdom among the raging flood waters for 150 days. He watched his kingdom crumble and all his wives and Nephilim children perish. And once God stopped the Flood, the waters of the deep returned underground ("And the waters returned from off the earth continually"), sucking the Assyrian and the other sinning angels down to the abyss, alive.

At the 5th trumpet judgment in the end times, the apostate Sons of God will be released from their imprisonment in the bottomless pit. They emerge as grotesque hybrid beings that the Bible calls "locusts":

> "And the fifth angel sounded, and I saw a star fall from heaven unto the earth: and to him was given the key of the bottomless pit. And he opened the bottomless pit; and there arose a smoke out of the pit, as the smoke of a great furnace; and the sun and the air were darkened by reason of the smoke of the pit. And there came out of the smoke locusts upon the earth: and unto them was given power, as the scorpions of the earth have power. And it was commanded them that they should not hurt the grass of the earth, neither any green thing, neither any tree; but only those men which have not the seal of God in their foreheads. **And to them it was given that they should not kill them, but that they should be tormented five months**: and their torment was as the torment of a scorpion, when he striketh a man.
>
> Revelation 9:1–11

The Bible records time according to the Hebrew calendar in which every month is 30 days. Thus, these locusts are released from Hell for 150 days to torment the earth as part of God's judgment – **the exact amount of time the Assyrian, the sinning angels, and their Nephilim sons were tormented by the Flood in the days of Noah.** Thus Scripture directly connects Ezekiel 31 to the Days of Noah as well as the end times.

6. What does Ezekiel 31 mean when Yahweh proclaims: "I have therefore delivered him into the hand of the mighty one of the heathen"? Provide Scripture to support your interpretation.

7. How does Ezekiel 31 connect to the "violence" that filled the earth in the days of Noah?

8. Using Scriptural evidence from Ezekiel 31, what was the ultimate punishment of the Assyrian, the Genesis 6 rebels and their Nephilim offspring?

Even though the Assyrian was wicked and doing the Devil's bidding, God nonetheless punished him by "delivering him into the hand of the mighty one of the heathen" – the Devil himself. The Adversary is loyal to no one and will destroy angel or human when given the opportunity. The notion of "delivering" someone to Satan for punishment was referenced twice by the Apostle Paul:

> "This charge I commit unto thee, son Timothy, according to the prophecies which went before on thee, that thou by them mightest war a good warfare; Holding faith, and a good conscience; which some having put away concerning faith have made shipwreck: Of whom is Hymenaeus and Alexander; whom I have delivered unto Satan, that they may learn not to blaspheme."
>
> **1 Timothy 1:18–20**

In the above passage someone who was supposed to be a follower of God defected from the faith or were in deep sin and was "delivered" to the Devil for bodily destruction as judgment. The Assyrian received the same punishment. His kingdom was engulfed in war, as the angels who envied him rose up to attack. The final days before the flood saw the angels and Nephilim hybrids attacking one another, plunging the earth into further ruin

This is confirmed by Genesis 6:

> **'The earth also was corrupt before God, and the earth was filled with violence**…And God said unto Noah, The end of all flesh is come before me; for the earth is filled with violence through them; and, behold, I will destroy them with the earth*"*
>
> **Genesis 6:11; 13**

The flood brought a stunning and cataclysmic end to this as the world war turned into a fight for survival against the divine tempests that covered the earth. After 150 days of flooding and witnessing their Nephilim offspring perish, the Assyrian and the rest of the Genesis 6 apostate angels were dragged down alive, into the abyss or bottomless pit:

> "I made the nations to shake at the sound of his fall, when I cast him down to hell with them that descend into the pit: and all the trees of Eden, the choice and best of Lebanon, all that drink water, shall be comforted in the nether parts of the earth. They also went down into hell with him unto them that be slain with the sword; and they that were his arm, that dwelt under his shadow in the midst of the heathen."
>
> **Ezekiel 31:16-17**

9. Name 4 similarities between the account of the Assyrian and the Genesis 6 incursion with the myth of Atlantis

GENESIS 6 WAS THE BASIS OF PAGAN MYTHOLOGY

Right alongside the heroes of Greek mythology was Plato's legend of Atlantis, a story that is still well-known today. Atlantis was a mythical island populated by gods and humans, full of wealth and advanced technology. As that society grew more evil, it was ultimately destroyed by a flood. First recorded in two dialogues by Plato called *Critias and Timaeus*, upon close examination it is apparent that the Atlantis myth was ultimately derived from the accounts of the Garden of Eden, Genesis 6, and the rise and fall of the Assyrian's hybrid kingdom as described in Ezekiel 31:

- Poseidon, a Greek god, fell in love with a human woman and impregnated her. Atlantis was built as the place for his bride and hybrid family to live.
- The island city of Atlantis was abundant with gold and other precious minerals. Genesis 2 identifies the precious metals in Eden:

    "…where there is gold; And the gold of that land is good: there is bdellium and the onyx stone."

    Genesis 2:12

- Atlantis had animals of "every kind." In Genesis 2 The Lord brings every animal to the Garden of Eden for Adam to name (Genesis 2:19-20).
- The Atlanteans benefits from the hot and cold springs and abundant waters of their island. Ezekiel 31 strongly emphasizes the strategic advantage the Assyrian held in the preflood world because his kingdom was situated by "waters":

"The waters made him great, the deep set him up on high with her rivers running round about his plants, and sent her little rivers unto all the trees of the field. Therefore his height was exalted above all the trees of the field, and his boughs were multiplied, and his branches became long **because of the multitude of waters**, when he shot forth… Thus was he fair in his greatness, in the length of his branches: **for his root was by great waters."**

Ezekiel 31:4–5; 7

- And of course, in the Atlantis myth, the hybrid kingdom was destroyed by a flood after the "gods" were committing too much evil in their interactions and marriages with humanity. This is a clear retelling of the fornication between the Sons of God and the daughters of men, corrupting human genetics, birthing the Nephilim and unleashing unprecedented evil in the world.

10. Ezekiel 31 presents an entirely new fallen angel to much of the Christian community: the Assyrian. 1) How do the accounts of Ezekiel 31 and 32 affect your view of the importance of the Nephilim in Scripture? 2) Why do you think this chapter is so rarely discussed or written on in the Church today? 3) Why is it or is it not important for the Church to learn these aspects of Scripture?

11. List 4 details from the Book of Enoch that contradict the Bible

12. What is problematic about the role the apocryphal book gives to Enoch? Provide a specific reference from the Book of Enoch

Perhaps no other book has played a greater role in the resurgence of interest in the Days of Noah as the Book of Enoch. The modern generation of Bible researchers, Christians and paranormal fans exploring these concepts often credit the Book of Enoch as one of their primary sources. And while it is a valuable historical resource and was certainly used in the ancient Jewish community in Judea in the centuries before the First Advent of The Lord Jesus Christ, the Book of Enoch was not a divinely inspired book and contains a number of verses that contradict Scripture.

For example, it claims to be written by Enoch, despite its first emerging in the ancient Hebrew community thousands of years after Enoch was raptured.

Additionally, the Bibles makes absolutely no reference to a book written by Enoch. In the early days of the nation of Israel, there were several occasions where the entire cannon of recorded Scripture up to that point was read aloud to the nation. And in each instance, the "Bible" of ancient Israel commenced with the books of Moses:

> **"And Moses came and told the people all the words of the LORD, and all the judgments:** and all the people answered with one voice, and said,

All the words which the LORD hath said will we do. **And Moses wrote all the words of the LORD,** and rose up early in the morning, and builded an altar under the hill, and twelve pillars, according to the twelve tribes of Israel. And he sent young men of the children of Israel, which offered burnt offerings, and sacrificed peace offerings of oxen unto the LORD. And Moses took half of the blood, and put it in basons; and half of the blood he sprinkled on the altar. **And he took the book of the covenant, and read in the audience of the people**: and they said, All that the LORD hath said will we do, and be obedient."

Exodus 24:3–7

The "book of the covenant" Moses read were his own writings as contained in the first five books of the Bible. This was "the Bible" for many centuries of ancient Hebrew history. When Joshua recorded and recited all Scripture for the Israelites, it was only "the law" – the writings of Moses (Joshua 8:30-35). And when Jesus read the Old Testament to His disciples, we are told it was done "…beginning at Moses." (Luke 24:25-27).

The Book of Enoch also contradicts the Biblical timeline as it has Enoch witness the birth of Noah (1 Enoch 107:2-3). In the Biblical timeline, Noah is born 69 years after Enoch was translated. Additionally in the Book of Enoch, it was not Satan who deceived Eve, but a different angel named Gadreel (1 Enoch 69:6).

One of the most egregious contradictions to the Bible is where the Book of Enoch states that it was angels who built the ark – not Noah:

"And in those days the word of God came unto me, and He said unto me: 'Noah, thy lot has come up before Me, a lot without blame, a lot of love and uprightness. **And now the angels are making a wooden (building), and when they have completed that task I will place My hand upon it and preserve it, and there shall come forth from it the seed of life,** and a change shall set in so that the earth will not remain without inhabitant.

And I will make fast thy seed before me for ever and ever, and I will spread abroad those who dwell with thee: it shall not be unfruitful on the face of the earth, but it shall be blessed and multiply on the earth in the name of the Lord.'"

Pseudo-Enoch 67:1–3

The construction of the ark was not just salvation for Noah and his family, it was a testimony to his great faith in God. In Genesis 6, God provides the dimensions of the ark, commands Noah to build it and:

"Thus did Noah; according to all that God commanded him, so did he."

Genesis 6:22

Pseudo-Enoch also credits the angels with warning Noah about the flood, not Yahweh. And in one of the more shocking passages, the Book of Enoch depicts angels asking Enoch to petition God for their forgiveness. (Pseudo-Enoch 13:1-7) and The Lord also asking Enoch to intercede on behalf of the fallen angels. (Pseudo-Enoch 15:1-2).

13. Name 3 of the teachings in the Book of Enoch that can be considered heresy. How do they contradict the Bible?

14. If the Book of Enoch is not divinely inspired like the Bible, how can we explain the quote from it we find in Jude? What examples are there of Biblical authors quoting works that were not inspired?

TROUBLING TEACHINGS IN THE BOOK OF ENOCH

The Bible encourages Christians to "…prove all things." (1 Thessalonians 5:21). We are to examine ancient texts through the lens of Scripture – confirming that they are aligned with the Divinely-inspired Word of God. In the case of the Book of Enoch there are some verses that are not only contrary to Scripture, but teach concepts that are heretical:

- It depicts righteous men praying to angels instead of God for blessing. (1 Enoch 9:1-3), something the Bible expressly prohibits:

> "Let no man beguile you of your reward in a voluntary humility and worshipping of angels, intruding into those things which he hath not seen, vainly puffed up by his fleshly mind…"
> **Colossians 2:18**

- It gives praise to the tree of the knowledge of good and evil – the one tree The Lord warned Adam that if he or Eve ate from it, they would "surely die." (Pseudo-Enoch 32:3-6).

- The Book of Enoch encourages offerings be made to the sun, moon and stars:

> "10 And now, know ye that from the angels He will inquire as to your deeds in heaven, from the sun and from the moon and from the stars in reference to your sins because upon the earth ye execute judgement on the righteous. 11. And He will summon to testify against you every cloud and mist and dew and rain; for they shall all be withheld because of you from descending upon you, and they shall be mindful of your sins. 12. And now give presents to the rain that it be not withheld from descending upon you, nor yet the dew, when it has received gold and silver from you that it may descend. 13. When the hoar-frost and snow with their chilliness, and all the snow-storms with all their plagues fall upon you, in those days ye shall not be able to stand before them"
> **Pseudo-Enoch 100:10-13**

This is a dangerous teaching. The Bible strictly forbids any worship being given to the sun, stars, planets or any heavenly body (Deuteronomy 4:16-19). Any encouragement to worship someone or something other than God is heresy.

WHAT ABOUT THE VERSE IN JUDE?

The most cited and strongest evidence supporting the validity of the Book of Enoch is that the book of Jude quotes from it:

> **"And Enoch also, the seventh from Adam, prophesied of these, saying,** Behold, the Lord cometh with ten thousands of his saints, To execute judgment upon all, and to convince all that are ungodly among them of all their ungodly deeds which they have ungodly committed, and of all their hard speeches which ungodly sinners have spoken against him."
> **Jude 1:14–15**

> "And behold! He cometh with ten thousands of His holy ones to execute judgment upon all, and to destroy all the ungodly: and to convict all flesh of all the works of their ungodliness which they have ungodly committed, and of all the hard things which ungodly sinners have spoken against Him."
> **Book of Enoch 1:9**

So how can the use of the book be explained? There are several ways:

- All Scripture is given by inspiration of God. (2 Timothy 3:16). Jude could have been inspired to write that prophecy of Enoch.

- The quote could have been in a non-canonical book – whether it be the Book of Enoch or one of the many apocryphal texts in circulation in 1st century Judea. If so, it would not be the only time such a thing was done in the Bible. When the Apostle Paul, moved by the Holy Spirit, preached the Gospel in the city of Athens, he cited a pagan poet: "For in him we live, and move, and have our being; as certain also of your own poets have said, For we are also his offspring" (Acts 17:28). This was a quote of the Greek poet Aratus.

In 1 Corinthians 15:33, Paul wrote: "ᴮᵉ not deceived: evil communications corrupt good manners," a quote from *Thais*, a work by the Greek poet Menander. Titus 1:12 states: "One of themselves, even a prophet of their own, said, the Cretans are always liars, evil beasts, slow bellies. This witness is true," quoting the poem *Paradox* by Epimenides, a Cretan poet. In all these instances, the Holy Spirit used truths from uninspired, non-biblical texts to compose Scripture.

- Jude referencing a dispute between the archangel Michael and Satan over the body of Moses gives further evidence to the notion that Jude had access to texts that are no longer extant.

15. Many people have come to view the Book of Enoch as a trusted source - even on par with the Bible itself. How do you view the book's inspiration? How would you explain the Book of Enoch's proper place in canon to someone who sees the book as divinely inspired?

16. What does the Book of Jasher state about Moses that contradicts the Bible? Why is this problematic?

17. What does the Book of Jasher teach about Joseph that is a contradiction to Scripture? Why is this problematic?

In even more disturbing fashion, the Book of Jasher, which has significantly less provenance than the Book of Enoch, contains flagrant contradictions and heresies that all Christians should be wary of. In its account of the Exodus, it depicts a teenage Moses fleeing Egypt to become a king in Cush, ruling and waging war. (Jasher 72:21–23, 34).

The Apostle Stephen refuted this account in Acts 7 when he recounted the life of Moses – with Moses living in Egypt for 40 years before fleeing to Midian as a fugitive after he killed an Egyptian man in an attempt to liberate the Israelites. (Acts 7:22-5; 29-30). Additionally, the Jasher fabrications undermine the powerful demonstration of faith Moses made by giving up his prestige and power as Egyptian royalty to be with his own people: the Israelites:

> "By faith Moses, when he was come to years, refused to be called the son
> of Pharaoh's daughter; Choosing rather to suffer affliction with the people
> of God, than to enjoy the pleasures of sin for a season; Esteeming the
> reproach of Christ greater riches than the treasures in Egypt: for he had
> respect unto the recompence of the reward. By faith he forsook Egypt, not
> fearing the wrath of the king: for he endured, as seeing him who is

invisible."

Rather than seeking a crown in Cush, Moses forsook high society to suffer with Israel. And he did this because of his faith in Yahweh and the promise of the prophesied Redeemer: Christ.

But the worst passage in Jasher involves its account of Joseph. The apocryphal text depicts Joseph – one of the most powerful foreshadows of Jesus Christ, and one of the greatest examples of faithful believers in God, committing the sin of necromancy, by praying to his deceased mother. And not only does Joseph pray to her, but Rebekah also responds from the grave! This is occult activity that The Lord called "an abomination" in Deuteronomy 18.

7. NEPHILIM AFTER THE FLOOD

CHAPTERS 13-14

How did the Giants return after the flood? Was there a second incursion by the fallen angels? Or did the genetics of the Nephilim somehow make it through the ark? This is one of the great debates when it comes to Genesis 6. And the Bible provides significant evidence for Nephilim DNA making it through the flood via the ark.

KEY THEMES:

- Noah stepping off the ark was a repetition of the creation of humanity and foreshadow of the New Earth that will be created at the return of Christ.
- All of the postdiluvian Nephilim can be traced back to Canaan, the son of Ham.
- Once the world was dispersed at the Tower of Babel rebellion, God resolved to turn the nations over to the fallen angels and create His own nation through one man - Abraham.

1. What was Rev. Samuel Maitland's view on how the Nephilim returned after the flood? Do you agree or disagree? Explain why or why not.

2. How old was Noah when he had his first son? Why is this significant with respect to the emergence of Nephilim after the flood?

NEPHILIM DNA TRAVELED ON THE ARK

"For my own part, however, I see no reason why Ishbi-benob may not have been personally and lineally descended from the 'Sons of God' whosoever they may have been. Some people were, I suppose, and why not he? We must consider, that though the Ark contained only one family, consisting of but eight souls yet in all probability that family represented five lines of pedigree. The Patriarch Noah, it may be remembered, was himself of the family of Seth. Whatever idea we may have of his personal holiness, and of the antediluvian piety of his sons, we are not, I suppose, authorised to assume that by something amounting almost to a miracle, the several lines of Noah himself, of his wife, and of his three daughters-in-law – lines going back perhaps through many ages and generations – were all kept pure from any mixture of giant blood." – *False Worship: An Essay*, Rev. Dr. Samuel Maitland, Published in London: Rivingtons, Waterloo Place, 1856, pp. 21–23.

There is something fascinating about Noah's lineage – he had his first child at age 500. This was a vastly older age than any of the patriarchs before him. Why does this matter? We know from Scripture, that Noah boarded the ark at age 600. Genesis 6 also confirms that God gave the earth a 120-year probation when He instructed Noah to build the ark (when Noah would have been 480 years old). Thus, by the time Noah had his sons, Shem, Ham and Japheth – the odds of them finding a wife who was 100% free of any Nephilim DNA was minimal.

And when one takes into account that Ham, the wicked son of Noah, would have no regard or concern for the Ultimate Prophecy or the Coming Messiah, he certainly would have no issue taking a wife who possessed Nephilim DNA. Reverend Samuel Maitland concurred with this interpretation as did much of the early church.

THE NEW WORLD

3. **List 4 of the similarities between the Creation Week of Genesis chapters 1 and 2 and the Post-flood world once Noah and his family stepped out of the ark in Genesis 9**

There are many striking parallels between the account of Noah entering the newly restarted Earth and Adam in the Garden of Eden:

- Both Genesis 9 and the creation week start with the earth covered in water. Both stories involved animals supernaturally gathered to God's chosen servant (Genesis 2:19; 7:9).

- In the Creation week, the Holy Spirit (who in the New Testament took the form of a dove – Matthew 3:16) hovered above the waters of the earth before land appeared. In Genesis 8, Noah released a dove to fly above the waters in search for land.

- Humanity was once again granted dominion over those animals (Genesis 1:26; Genesis 9:2).

- The Lord reinforced to Adam and Noah the creation truth that man was unique from all other creatures as he was made in the image of God (Genesis 1:26; 9:6).

- Humans were to be fruitful and multiply to replenish the earth.

- Both stories include sin involving fruit (the forbidden fruit, the wine drunk by Noah).

- Both stories involve nakedness that needed to be covered (Genesis 3:7; Genesis 9:23).

THE MYSTERY OF CANAAN

4. **What could have been a reason that Noah cursed Canaan instead of Ham – even though Ham sinned against him?**

5. **What Biblical evidence confirms the importance of the name "Canaan" in Biblical history?**

6. **How does the location of Canaan's descendants after the Tower of Babel rebellion factor into the war of the bloodlines of the Messiah and Seed of the Serpent?**

Canaan, the son of Ham, is one of the most mysterious figures in the Bible. His name is mentioned an astounding 157 times in Scripture – despite the fact that that none of his words or actions are ever recorded. Such an omission is eerily similar to the abrupt end of the lineage of Cain in Genesis 4 after the family of Lamech and his children Jabal, Jubal, Tubal-Cain, and Naamah. Scripture has no interest in promoting the Nephilim or their life stories. Their presence is mentioned only as it serves to reveal God's glory and plan of salvation. This gives greater weight to the notion that the Nephilim gene survived the Flood through Ham's wife and then his sons, particularly Canaan.

Twice in Genesis 9 we are told that Ham was "the father of Canaan" – affirming Canaan's infamy in ancient Hebrew society. One of the greater mysteries of the Bible was why Noah cursed Canaan for Ham's sin. Canaan was the father of all the postdiluvian giants. From a literal reading of Scripture, it is clear that Ham's wife must have carried the corrupted DNA that passed through the Flood. The presence of the Nephilim gene may have caused Canaan to appear different from his siblings and cousins to the point that Noah knew some trace of the antediluvian genetic corruption was in him – something the Bible noted with respect to other siblings who were descendants of giants (2 Samuel 21:20). This would explain both the special reference to Canaan and the curse placed upon him rather than upon his father, Ham.

Following the Tower of Babel rebellion and the dispersal of different nations, all of Canaan's descendants settled in the Promised Land – the very territory God designated for the Israelites to inhabit and location of His Holy Mountain. This was no coincidence. In the ongoing chess match between Yahweh and the Devil, the forefather of the postdiluvian Nephilim saw his offspring beat God's chosen nation to the most valuable land on the planet. If God's Promise was going to be fulfilled, His people would have to go through the giants first.

7. **Citing Dr. Michael Heiser, provide an interpretation of Deuteronomy 32:8-9 and 4:19. How do these verses explain aspects of the angelic realm?**

8. **What does Daniel chapter 10 teach us about angelic principalities?**

After Nimrod's failed revolution at Babel, God divided the world into 70 nations (listed in Genesis 11). Nimrod and his fellow rebels dispersed all over the globe. Shem, Noah's first son, carried on the Messianic bloodline and remained in the Middle East. Those who opposed the Lord wanted to "make a name" for themselves. Shem, the son of Noah, was called "the name" (the Hebrew meaning of his name). In Jewish writing, the Lord is referred to as "*Hashem*" or "the Name." Faithful believers such as Shem would bear the blessing of God that the heathen world so desperately longed for.

There was also a division among the heavenly realm as God divided authority over the nations between He and the fallen angels – giving all of the Gentile countries to the principalities while keeping Israel as His "portion":

> "When the Most High divided the nations, when he separated the sons of
> Adam, he set the bounds of the nations according to the number of the
> angels of God. And his people Jacob became the portion of the Lord,

Israel was the line of his inheritance."

Deuteronomy 32:8–9 LXX

"And lest thou lift up thine eyes unto heaven, and when thou seest the sun, and the moon, and the stars, even all the host of heaven, shouldest be driven to worship them, and serve them, which the LORD thy God hath divided unto all nations under the whole heaven."

Deuteronomy 4:19

Dr. Michael Heiser agreed with this understanding:

"Deuteronomy 4:19–20 and 32:8 present two sides of the same coin. In Deuteronomy 32:8–9, God apportions the nations to the sons of God; here [in Deuteronomy 4:19], however, God allots the gods to the nations. Israelites, in other words, believed that Yahweh, their own supreme, unique God, sentenced the nations and their gods to each other. At Babel, God, like a father dismissing and disinheriting his children, judges all the nations for their disobedience (Gen 11:1–9). Then, in the very next chapter, He calls Abraham (Gen 12:1–3), effectively starting over in creating an earthly human family for Himself."

– http://www.thedivinecouncil.com/Deuteronomy32OTWorldview.pdf

ONE MAN AGAINST THE WORLD

9. **What was God's plan with Abraham? How did those pose a danger to the Messianic Bloodline?**

10. Abraham lying about Sarah being his sister often seems like a "strange little story" from his life. But explain the importance of that account in light of the war between the two bloodlines. What led Abraham into this dilemma?

11. What was the reason for Abraham's conflict with Lot? What does its resolution reveal about Abraham? What was the danger of Lot's decision?

The Lord does not require large human armies and forces to bring forth His will. With just one faithful man, God was going to create His own nation that would bring the Light of the glorious Gospel of salvation in the Messiah and preserve the lineage leading to His birth. And that man was Abraham.

From the fallen angelic perspective the Adversary now had one specific target to focus on in order to disrupt The Lord's plan of redemption. If Satan could destroy or corrupt Abraham, it could jeopardize the Messianic bloodline. Hence, the famine which caused Abraham, in fear, to leave the land of Canaan (where The Lord dispatched him) and seek refuge in Egypt. There Satan used the Pharaoh's lust for Sarah for his own purpose. Again, in fear, Abraham lied and told the Egyptian monarch that Sarah was his sister, not his wife. This led to Pharaoh almost taking Sarah as his bride, which would have thwarted God's prophecy that Abraham's seed would be birthed by her.

The Lord intervened with supernatural plagues to frighten the Egyptian king and protect the bloodline of the Savior. Note the love of God – even when Abraham sinned, The Lord still defended him and our salvation.

The dispute between the laborers of Abraham and Lot revealed the heart and character of Abraham. Rather than continue the conflict or be greedy with his land, Abraham deferred to his nephew – allowing Lot to choose territory he preferred – the plains of Jordan. The spiritual danger of Lot's choice was that this put him in proximity to the wicked city of Sodom, where he ultimately ended up living.

> **12. Understanding the roles fallen angels occupy over the nations of the world and their relentless attacks on God's people, how does this affect your view of world affairs and politics? Thinking about this and God's repeated deliverance of Abraham, what does it say about the challenges you go through in your own life? Use the space below to write a prayer for God's strength in the face of our fallen angelic enemies.**

8. THE NEPHILIM WORLD WAR

CHAPTERS 15-16

Genesis 14 records a fascinating account of a war of human armies versus Nephilim, with humans prevailing. God used this conflict to build Abraham's faith and prepare him to raise up a godly lineage.

KEY THEMES:

- Abraham's military victory was another powerful reminder that Yahweh reigns over all of the fallen angels and their Nephilim offspring.

- God's covenant with Abraham was premised on the conquest of the Nephilim in the land of Canaan.

- Satan is unrelenting in his wicked quest to conquer God's people and disrupt the plan of salvation.

- God will even take sinful decisions by His believers to work things together for the good and His Will.

A 3-PART CONFLICT

1. Explain the three phases of the Genesis 14 Nephilim war

2. What is the explanation for the many different tribes of Nephilim after flood? What major event led to their various names? What did all these tribes have in common?

3. Citing an ancient source, explain the meaning of the name "Zuzim." What were 2 characteristics of these giants?

4. What is the Biblical evidence that the Amorites were giants? Reading Genesis 10:15-16, what can we conclude about their heritage?

The Genesis 14 world war marks the first recorded battle of humans versus giants. The conflict was divided into 3 phases:

- In the first campaign, Chedorlaomer led his powerful confederacy southwards to attack Sodom. This campaign took the four-king coalition through the heart of giant-infested territory. Chedorlaomer's forces wiped out scores of giants on their march to Sodom, evidence of the overwhelming military forces at their disposal.

- With the Nephilim standing between them and their enemies defeated, the kings of Sodom, Gomorrah and their neighboring cities were forced to enter into the battle against Chedorlaomer's armies. They were defeated and abandoned their cities allowing the 4-king coalition to plunder Sodom. This is when Lot was kidnapped. (Genesis 14:10-12).

- In the third campaign, Abraham took 318 men, headed 100 miles north to Chedorlaomer's territory and slaughtered all the coalition forces, rescuing Lot in the process. (Genesis 14:15-17).

RISE OF THE POSTDILUVIAN GIANTS

In the Genesis 14 war we see the tribal names of the Nephilim who lived after the flood. The reason for their various names was due to the Tower of Babel dispersion in which God confused the languages. All of these giants were *Rephaim*. We see confirmation of this in Deuteronomy 2:

> "The Emims dwelt therein in times past, a people great, and many, and tall, as the Anakims; ^{Which} also were accounted giants [*Rephaim*], as the Anakims; but the Moabites called them Emims."
> **Deuteronomy 2:10-11**

All of these giant tribes – whether they were Emims, Zuzims or Amorites (among others) were "accounted" as Rephaim. And they possessed supernatural size and strength:

"That also was accounted a land of giants [*repahaim*]: giants dwelt therein in old time; and the Ammonites call them Zamzummims; A people great, and many, and tall, as the Anakims; but the LORD destroyed them before them; and they succeeded them, and dwelt in their stead…."

Deuteronomy 2:20–21

Johnathan Gill's *Exposition of the Bible* wrote of the Zuzims:

"They are thought to be the same with the Zuzims in (Genesis 14:5) who had their name, as Hillerus [E3] thinks, from Mezuzah, a door post, from their tall stature, being as high as one; and for a like reason Saph the giant might have his name, (2 Samuel 21:18). The word Zamzummims, according to him, signifies contrivers of evil and terrible things; they were inventors of wickedness, crafty and subtle in forming wicked and mischievous designs, which struck terror into people, and made them formidable to them." - http://www.studylight.org/commentaries/geb/Genesis-14.html

The Amorites, who were led by Nephilim kings Og and Sihon, are noted in Scripture for their enormous size:

"Yet destroyed I the Amorite before them, whose height was like the height of the cedars, and he was strong as the oaks; yet I destroyed his fruit from above, and his roots from beneath."

Amos 2:9

Not only does the passage confirm that they were giants, but it also provides greater evidence that Canaan was indeed the forefather of the postdiluvian Nephilim as the Amorites were his direct descendants. (Genesis 10:15-16).

5. **What did Melchizedek's prayer in Genesis 14:18-20 reveal about God's role in the Nephilim world war? what is the significance of the Hebrew term "*El Elyon*"?**

6. What was the importance of the covenant in Genesis 15:18-21? What did the nations mentioned share in common?

7. Why did Abraham make Eleazer take an oath regarding Isaac's wife?

8. Explain Robert Purdon's position on the postdiluvian Nephilim

GOD PROVIDES THE VICTORY

"And Melchizedek king of Salem brought forth bread and wine: and he was the priest of the most high God. And he blessed him, and said, Blessed be Abram of the most high God, possessor of heaven and earth: And blessed be the most high God, which hath delivered thine enemies into thy hand. And he gave him tithes of all."

Genesis 14:18–20

Chedorlaomer's coalition conquered cities filled with Nephilim. And yet, Abraham with just 318 servants, slaughtered them. How was Abraham able to achieve such a stunning upset victory? God fought for him. As is the case throughout Scripture, whenever Nephilim were involved, *the Lord personally intervened in battles* to ensure their destruction. This of course is a picture of salvation as Jesus Christ, the promised Seed of the Woman, went to battle for all humanity on the cross – defeating Satan, sin, and the grave once and for all. It is very important to keep this theme in mind. God provided the Flood. God fought for Abram. And God continued to fulfill the prophecy by personally waging war against the Nephilim until they were extinct.

Melchizedek's prayer is the first time we hear the title *"El Elyon"* or the Most High God. This was an acknowledgment of Yahweh ruling over all of the righteous angels and fallen rebels (who posed as the "gods" of the nations). Abraham affirmed this when he refused to accept any reward from the king of Sodom:

> "And Abram said to the king of Sodom, I have lift up mine hand unto the
> LORD, the most high God, the possessor of heaven and earth, That I will
> not take from a thread even to a shoe latchet, and that I will not take any
> thing that is thine, lest thou shouldest say, I have made Abram rich...."
> **Genesis 14:21–23**

After the military victory, The Lord entered into a covenant with Abraham to give him and his offspring the Promised Land. From Abraham's seed a great nation would be born who would reclaim God's territory from the Nephilim usurpers:

> "In the same day the LORD made a covenant with Abram, saying, Unto thy
> seed have I given this land, from the river of Egypt unto the great river, the
> river Euphrates: The Kenites, and the Kenizzites, and the Kadmonites, And
> the Hittites, and the Perizzites, and the Rephaims, And the Amorites, and
> the Canaanites, and the Girgashites, and the Jebusites."
> **Genesis 15:18–21**

All these nations were descendants of Canaan. The battle lines were drawn – the true battle was not just a wholesale slaughter of anyone in the Promised Land – it was a targeted expulsion of the postdiluvian Nephilim lineage. Abraham understood the genetic threat of the Canaanites. When making arrangements for a bride to be chosen for his son Isaac, who God promised would continue the Messianic bloodline, Abraham made his servant Eleazar take an oath, that Isaac's future wife would be from "his own kindred" and not from Canaan's descendants.

Even when Eleazar asked what to do if he could not find a suitable bride, Abraham promised that the Angel of The Lord would go before him to ensure his success. (Genesis 24:1-9). The very fate of humanity was at stake and God would again intercede to ensure our redemption was secure.

THE POST-FLOOD GIANTS WERE AN INFERIOR VERSION OF THE ORIGINAL NEPHILIM

As they were not born directly from the fallen angels, the postdiluvian giants did not have the same size and power of their forefathers, the original giants from the Days of Noah. Theologian Robert Purdon arrived at the same conclusion:

> "But though the Giants were destroyed the gigantic RACE (sp) remained. The children of the original Giants were Giants like their fathers: they were the grandsons of Angels – Giants at one remove – less by one degree than their parents, but greater by far than ordinary men. The heavenly blood still circulated in their veins and from them it was transmitted to posterity." – *The Last Vials: Being a Series of Essays Upon the Second Advent*, No. X, 22nd year, Sept. 1st, Robert A. Purdon, 1867, p. 6.

REBEKAH – AN UNSUNG HEROINE

9. **How did the conflict between Jacob and Esau relate to the war of the two bloodlines?**

10. Who were "the Daughters of Heth"? What was their connection to the war of the two bloodlines?

11. "And Rebekah said to Isaac, I am_____ because of the daughters of Heth: if _____ what good shall my life do me?" - Genesis 27:46

12. Explain Rebekah's deception of Isaac from the perspective of the war of the two bloodlines

Rebekah's deception of Isaac is another account from Biblical history that on its face may seem like an odd little story but in reality, held enormous importance. When she was pregnant with her twin sons, God pronounced to Rebekah that it would be Jacob, the younger, who would receive the Abrahamic blessing. Isaac, out of his own favoritism, wanted to pass on the blessing to Esau instead. The eventual conflict between the two brothers eventually put Jacob's life in danger, again bringing the Ultimate Prophecy into peril.

Rebekah had a keen understanding of this as she was grieved when Esau took two wives from the daughters of Heth. (Genesis 26:34-35). Heth was the second son of Canaan. Esau had little concern for his birthright or the Ultimate prophecy and thus had no qualms marrying two women even if it meant mingling the seed of the Woman with the postdiluvian Nephilim DNA. After the deception, Isaac finally came to his senses and sent Jacob away to find a bride from among the lineage of Abraham and forbade his sone from taking a bride from among the Canaanites.

JOSEPH – FORESHADOW OF JESUS CHRIST

13. **Provide 3 details from the lives of Joseph and Jesus that demonstrate Joseph was a foreshadow of Christ**

14. **Genesis 38 is often viewed as a random story placed in the middle of the account of the life of Joseph. With the war against the fallen angels and Nephilim as the proper context, how can we explain God's swift, devastating punishment of Judah's children?**

Joseph is a remarkable foreshadow of The Lord Jesus Christ. He was favored by his father and betrayed by his brothers (the patriarchs of the twelve tribes of Israel), was sold into slavery and punished for a crime he did not commit. However, he ultimately rose to such prominence that he sat at the right hand of Pharaoh as the second-most-powerful ruler in Egypt. He was also able to save Israel and many other nations of the world through his divinely endowed power of interpreting dreams. This was a foreshadow of Jesus Christ, who came to the twelve tribes who "received him not." Jesus was similarly punished unjustly, and in His death and resurrection, He won salvation for all who believe in Him.

THE SIN OF JUDAH

In the midst of the account of Joseph we find an interesting record of the sins of Judah. The son who was chosen to carry the direct lineage to the Messiah, Judah threw everything into jeopardy by taking a Canaanite woman as his wife:

> "And Judah saw there a daughter of a certain Canaanite, whose name was Shuah; and he took her, and went in unto her. And she conceived, and bare a son; and he called his name Er."
> **Genesis 38:1-3**

As were all the Nephilim and those who carried Nephilim genes, Er was "wicked in the sight of the Lord." This first son of Judah could have no part in the lineage that would lead to the Savior. And how did he die? *God killed him.* As would become a part of the Mosaic Law, if a married man died without having a child, his brother was to marry the widow. This law served to keep the nation of Israel growing while maintaining the genetic purity of the undefiled Messianic line. Onan, Judah's second son, violated this rule, leading to his death at the mighty hand of God.

Why such harsh judgment? The Lord was correcting the sinful errors of Judah. His actions introduced the Nephilim – tainted genes of Canaan's descendants – into the nation of Israel. So, the Lord personally slew the offspring of this union. It is critical to remember that in these early stages of the plan of salvation, this small family was the critical instrument in God's hand. Twelve brothers were holders of the fate of the nation of Israel and the future of the entire world. God thus dealt with sinful mistakes such as Judah's sharply and swiftly. This serves to reveal God's grace in fiercely protecting humanity.

9. BIRTH OF GOD'S NATION

CHAPTERS 17-18

The account of the life of Joseph sets the stage for the birth of the nation of Israel. God rescued the twelve tribes from oppression in Egypt. He then prepared the nation in the wilderness - training them spiritually for the war to come against the Nephilim-led nations in the Promised Land.

KEY THEMES:

- The Lord fulfills all His promises. It may not be at the time we think or hope it will happen, but all His promises come to pass.
- The Nephilim were so frightening that it took only 3 giants to cause a generation of Israelites to doubt God.
- The conflict between Jesus and the Devil is war. God fought for His people in ancient times, will fight again in the end times and still fights for you today.

1. What was the significance of Joseph's family being shepherds in the context of the war of the two bloodlines?

2. Once the nation of Israel started to grow and flourish in Egypt what was Satan's counterstrike to thwart God's plans?

3. Many theologians teach that the ten spies, (who delivered an "evil report" about the giants) lied to the Israelites - exaggerating the size of these Nephilim. How can we know from Scripture that the sons of Anak were in fact, superhuman-sized giants? Circle True or False next to each statement to answer this question:

The grapes cluster the spies found were so heavy they had to be carried by 2 men (Numbers 13:21-23)?   TRUE   FALSE

The spies encountered a massive army of hundreds of Nephilim (Numbers 13:22)?TRUE   FALSE

The giants were so famous that their father Anak was well-known among the Israelites (Numbers 13:22; 33)? TRUE   FALSE

The spies reported that the sons of Anak were twice the size of a human (Numbers 13:33)?   **TRUE**   **FALSE**

In prophetic foreshadow of the redemptive work of Christ, Joseph was able to save his entire family from famine and forgave them for their sins against him. Why does that even matter? It provided a strategic advantage in the war of the bloodlines. Within the confines of the most powerful empire on the planet, Israel's offspring grew into a populous nation. Handling cattle was offensive and revolting in ancient Egyptian culture. Thus, the Egyptians had no desire to have social or marital relations with the Israelite people who were shepherds. This development provided the Israelites many generations to grow as a people – from 70 to millions in the decades that followed – with no outside interference or threat of genetic corruption.

Several generations later, the Devil launched a counterstrike. With Joseph deceased and a Pharaoh who never knew Joseph in power, the suddenly populous nation of Israel posed a threat to the Egyptians. And the king sought to curb the rapid population growth of their Hebrew slaves by declaring a genocidal proclamation to kill all male Israelite children under the age of 2. (Exodus 1:8-10; 22). The Devil turned to human rulers to carry out his plan of wiping out the Seed of the Woman. If he could succeed in having every *male Israelite child* murdered, then potentially the Messiah would be dead or his lineage ruined.

THE PROVOCATION – THE NEPHILIM CAUSE ISRAEL TO DOUBT GOD

Following Yahweh's spectacular, supernatural deliverance of Israel from Egyptian bondage via the plagues of the Exodus, the twelve tribes headed through the wilderness to enter the Promised Land. When Moses dispatched 12 spies to scout the land, they encountered Ahiman, Sheshai and Talmai, the sons of Anak. These Nephilim giants were so frightening, ten of the spies did not believe The Lord could overcome them and give the Promised Land to His chosen nation.

Many commentaries and teachings on the passage describe the ten spies as lying about the size of the sons of Anak – as opposed to them being truly supernaturally-sized postdiluvian Nephilim. However, the Old Testament repeatedly emphasized the sons of Anak and all his descendants, known as the Anakim, were in fact, giants:

> "That also was accounted a land of giants [rephaim]: giants dwelt therein in old time; and the Ammonites call them Zamzummims; A people great, and many, and tall, **as the Anakims**; but the LORD destroyed them before them; and they succeeded them, and dwelt in their stead...."
> **Deuteronomy 2:20–21**

> "Hear, O Israel: Thou art to pass over Jordan this day, to go in to possess nations greater and mightier than thyself, cities great and fenced up to heaven, A people great and tall, the children of the Anakims, whom thou knowest, and of whom thou hast heard say, Who can stand before the children of Anak!"
> **Deuteronomy 9:1–2**

The sons of Anak were the tribe by whom other groups of Nephilim were measured. They resided in Hebron, which Scripture confirms was "built seven years before Zoan in Egypt" (Numbers 13:22). Hebron was the oldest city in the known world, and it was originally known as Kirjath-Arba, in honor of Arba, the grandfather of Ahiman, Sheshai, and Talmai (Joshua 14:15).

In addition to their legendary size, even their agriculture was enormous. Numbers 13:21-23 reveals that it took two men using a pole to carry one cluster of grapes from Nephilim territory.

4. Read Hebrews 3:7-19. The "Provocation" of Numbers 13 was such a tragic event that an entire generation of Israelites died as a punishment. 1) Why was God so angered by this sin? 2) How does Hebrews 3 apply this event to the doctrine of salvation? 3) What does

this say about your faith in times when the trials of life seem impossible to overcome?

GATEKEEPERS OF THE PROMISED LAND

5. Using 2 sources, cite the Biblical evidence that King Sihon was a Nephilim

6. What was significant about the location of the Amorite kingdoms?

7. How were Sihon's armies defeated?

8. Explain: 1) Why would God command that the Amorites be "utterly" exterminated? 2) How can a loving God order "genocide"? 3) How does understanding Genesis 6 shape your view on the wars in the Promised Land?

9. Using 2 sources, cite Biblical evidence that King Og of Bashan was a Nephilim giant

10. Provide scriptural or scholarly evidence of the superior construction ability of the Nephilim

11 What great biblical events are the victories over kings Og and Sihon compared to (cite a scriptural source)?

A MAN OF WAR

"The Lord is a man of war: the Lord is his name."
Exodus 15:3

When the 40-year wilderness punishment ended, the younger generation of Israelites were ready to wage war against the giant-infested Canaanite kingdoms. The Lord's strategy required them to pass through the land of Og and Sihon – imposing Nephilim kings who were "Gate Keepers" into God's country. Their kingdoms sat due east of the Dead Sea, Jordan River, and Sea of Galilee, controlling access into the Promised Land. Centuries earlier, this area was overrun with giants.

As Israel arrived at his borders, Sihon immediately marshalled for war:

> "And Sihon would not suffer Israel to pass through his border: but Sihon
> gathered all his people together, and went out against Israel into the
> wilderness: and he came to Jahaz, and fought against Israel."
>
> *Numbers 21:21–23*

Amos 2:9 confirms that Sihon's height was "as the cedars." This was combat against the seed of the Serpent and it was God who led the armies of Israel:

> "And the LORD said unto me, Behold, I have begun to give Sihon and his land
> before thee: begin to possess, that thou mayest inherit his land. Then Sihon came
> out against us, he and all his people, to fight at Jahaz. And the LORD our God
> delivered him before us; and we smote him, and his sons, and all his people. And
> we took all his cities at that time, and utterly destroyed the men, and the women,
> and the little ones, of every city, we left none to remain:"
>
> *Deuteronomy 2:31-16*

For all Sihon's military prowess, the mighty warrior giant fell before the Lord. Every step of the way, God went out in front of the Israelite army to fight the initial battle and severely cripple the enemy so they could finish the job (Deuteronomy 2:33 includes the detail that the 12 tribes *also killed Sihon's sons*, eliminating his genetic line). The Lord was specifically and personally involved in destroying the remaining Nephilim giants off the face of the earth, fulfilling the Genesis 3:15 prophecy of enmity between the divine and satanic seeds. Jesus Christ, in His pre-incarnate form, was waging war against the Nephilim.

The *cherem* continued against King Og – who was also confirmed as a giant.

"For only Og king of Bashan remained of the remnant of giants; behold his bedstead was a bedstead of iron; is it not in Rabbath of the children of Ammon? nine cubits was the length thereof, and four cubits the breadth of it, after the cubit of a man."

Deuteronomy 3:11

The ancient Middle Eastern cubit measured anywhere from 18–21 inches meaning Og even by conservative estimates was approximately 13 feet tall. He was also the last of the Nephilim who were still called "Rephaim" by the people of that area of the Babel dispersion. Og's kingdom consisted of 60 cities (Deuteronomy 3:4). This massive megalopolis was testament to the superior construction ability of the giants. In both their agriculture and edifices, the Bible confirms the Nephilim possessed superhuman ability. A 19th century commentary concurred:

> "…when we see houses built of such huge and massive stones that no force that could ever have been brought against them would have been sufficient to batter them down; when we find rooms in these houses so large and so lofty, that many of them would be considered fine rooms in a large house in Europe; and lastly, when we find some of these towns bearing the very name that cities in that country bore before the Israelites came out of Egypt, I think we cannot help feeling the strongest conviction that we have before us the cities of the giant Rephaim." – *A Cyclopædia of Biblical Geography, Biography, Natural History, and General Knowledge*, Vol. 1, J. Lawson and J.M. Wilson, A. Fullerton & Co., 1866, p. 141–142.

In the face of this immense military force, their 60-city megalopolis, and hybrid king, the Lord told the Israelites "fear him not" (Deuteronomy 3:2). He sent his "hornet" to drive Og out of his impenetrable fortress into the open battlefield where He defeated them "…not with thy sword, nor with thy bow." (Joshua 24:12).

These wars were Jesus' battle to correct the genetic sins committed against humanity and preserve the Messianic bloodline. Salvation itself was at stake. And the victories over Og and Sihon were so momentous and critical to The Lord's redemption, they were even compared to God's victory at the Exodus:

"...Whatsoever the LORD pleased, that did he in heaven, and in earth, in the seas, and all deep places. He causeth the vapours to ascend from the ends of the earth; he maketh lightnings for the rain; he bringeth the win out of his treasuries. Who smote the firstborn of Egypt, both of man and beast. Who sent tokens and wonders into the midst of thee, O Egypt, upon Pharaoh, and upon all his servants. Who smote great nations, and slew mighty kings; Sihon king of the Amorites, and Og king of Bashan, and all the kingdoms of Canaan: And gave their land for an heritage, an heritage unto Israel his people."
Psalm 135:1–2, 6–12

THE ANGEL OF THE LORD

12. **Citing 2 sources (Biblical and/or ancient writers), explain the identity of the "Angel of The Lord" in the Old Testament**

13. **"And as soon as we had heard these things, our _____, neither did there remain any more courage in any man, because of you: for the Lord your God, _____ _____" - Joshua 2:11**

14. **What was the purpose of the parting of the Jordan river in Joshua 3:7-17?**

15. **Explain 3 parallels between the battle of Jericho and the flood in the days of Noah**

Jesus Christ is the Angel Of The Lord in the Old Testament. The appearances of the preincarnate Christ are also known as a "Christophany." This is confirmed in several passages, Exodus 3 being among them:

> "**And the angel of the LORD appeared unto him in a flame of fire out of the midst of a bush**: and he looked, and, behold, the bush burned with fire, and the bush was not consumed. And Moses said, I will now turn aside, and see this great sight, why the bush is not burnt. **And when the LORD saw that he turned aside to see, God called unto him out of the midst of the bush**, and said, Moses, Moses. And he said, Here am I. And he said, Draw not nigh hither: put off thy shoes from off thy feet, for the place whereon thou standest is holy ground. **Moreover he said, I am the God of thy father, the God of Abraham, the God of Isaac, and the God of Jacob**. And Moses hid his face; for he was afraid to look upon God."
>
> **Exodus 3:2–6**

Theologians from centuries past agreed:

> "We read 'Behold, I send an angel before thee, to keep thee in the way, and to bring thee into the place which I have prepared.' 'Mine angel shall go before thee and bring thee into the land of Canaan' (Exodus 23:20; 23). Surely this Angel of God was no other than Jehovah Jesus." – *Twelve Sermons*

Preached at Verulam District Church, Lambeth, London, Third Series, The Rev. J. Battetrsby, Fisher & Sidstone, 23, Morgate Street, London, 1878, p. 17.

It was Jesus Christ who routed the armies of Og and Sihon. This should underscore the cataclysmic threat the Nephilim posed to mankind that The Savior personally entered the earthly realm to wage war on our behalf.

CROSSING JORDAN – GOD PROMISES TO FIGHT FOR US

Though not as well-known as the similar miracle of the Red Sea, the parting of the Jordan River was a supernatural act of God and sign of His promise to deliver Israel. Joshua 3 makes this clear:

> "…Come hither, and hear the words of the LORD your God. **And Joshua said, Hereby ye shall know that the living God is among you, and that he will without fail drive out from before you the Canaanites, and the Hittites, and the Hivites, and the Perizzites, and the Girgashites, and the Amorites, and the Jebusites**. Behold, the ark of the covenant of the LORD of all the earth passeth over before you into Jordan. Now therefore take you twelve men out of the tribes of Israel, out of every tribe a man. And it shall come to pass, as soon as the soles of the feet of the priests that bear the ark of the LORD, the LORD of all the earth, shall rest in the waters of Jordan, that the waters of Jordan shall be cut off from the waters that come down from above; and they shall stand upon an heap."
>
> **Joshua 3:9-13**

The supernatural division of the Jordan river was Yahweh's confirmation that He indeed could and would destroy the seven Nephilim-contaminated nations in the land of Canaan. Just as The Lord judged them in the days of Noah. Note the parallels:

- Both judgments were supernatural events sent directly from God.

- Noah preached for 120 years while constructing the ark. Then The Lord instructed him to stay inside the ark for seven days before the Flood commenced. The rebellious antediluvians no longer heard God's Word and then judgment came. At Jericho, God instructed the Israelites to march around the city for six days in silence. Then on the seventh day they were to march seven times and shout, unleashing the judgment of God on the city. (Joshua 6:20-24).

- The flood wiped out the entire global population save for faithful Noah and his family. The destruction of Jericho destroyed the city's entire population save for faithful Rahab and her family.

WAR FOR THE PROMISED LAND

16. Circle True or False for the following statements:

The Israelites lured the people of Ai out of the city and then God destroyed it supernaturally (Joshua 8:15-21)
TRUE   FALSE

Joshua built altars on Mt. Ebal and Mt. Gerizim and divided the nation in half on each mount to recite the law (Joshua 8:30-35)   TRUE   FALSE

Adonizedec formed a coalition to attack the Gibeonites for making peace with Israel (Joshua 10:1-5)   TRUE   FALSE

When Joshua ascended up to Gilgal, The Lord instructed him to make peace with Adonizedec's confederacy (Joshua 10:20-26)   TRUE   FALSE

Joshua instructed the Israelites to put their feet on the necks of their enemies as a picture of what god will do to all who oppose him (Joshua 10:22-26)   TRUE   FALSE

17. Who were the 5 kings of the northern Canaan coalition that planned to attack the Israelites in Joshua 11:1-5?

18. "And they went out,_____

much people, even_____

_____, with horses and chariots very many." - Joshua 11:4

19. What is the spiritual significance of Joshua and Moses combining to defeat 33 Nephilim kings in the war for the promised land? See Joshua 12:24; Revelation 12:1-4

Joshua was one of the greatest leaders in Biblical history. His faith and obedience rank up with all of the most notable servants of Jesus Christ. After the battle of Jericho, he followed God on a rapid conquest of dozens of Nephilim-filled territories to recapture the Promised Land. At the battle of Ai, Joshua fooled the Canaanites by sending a small force who pretended they were losing the battle. Once the enemies left their city to chase down the retreating Israelites, The Lord commanded Joshua to stretch his spear towards Ai so He could "give it into his hand" – Yahweh supernaturally delivered the victory. (Joshua 8:15-21).

After winning the battle with divine assistance, Joshua responded by building an altar to God. He then divided the nation in half and had them stand on two adjacent mountains — Ebal and Gerizim. And there he wrote the law of Moses on stone tablets and read it in its entirety to the nation. (Joshua 8:30-35). This is a perfect model as to how we should show our thankfulness and recommit ourselves to The Lord when we receive a great blessing from Him.

Following the victory at AI, the Gibeonites tricked the twelve tribes into a peace accord. This angered Adonizedec, the king of Jerusalem and leader of the Southern Coalition of giant-contaminated cities:

> "Wherefore Adonizedec king of Jerusalem, sent unto Hoham king
> of Hebron, and unto Piram king of Jarmuth, and unto Japhia king
> of Lachish, and unto Debir king of Eglon, saying, Come up unto
> me, and help me, that we may smite Gibeon: for it hath made peace
> with Joshua and with the children of Israel. Therefore the five kings
> of the Amorites, the king of Jerusalem, the king of Hebron, the
> king of Jarmuth, the king of Lachish, the king of Eglon, gathered
> themselves together, and went up, they and all their hosts, and
> encamped before Gibeon, and made war against it."
>
> **Joshua 10:1–5**

When Joshua received news that the enemy was preparing to attack he ascended from his base of operations at Gilgal and God instructed him to enter battle where The Lord could personally conquer the Amorite Nephilim-led forces:

> "And the LORD discomfited them before Israel, and slew them
> with a great slaughter at Gibeon, and chased them along the way
> that goeth up to Bethhoron, and smote them to Azekah, and unto
> Makkedah."
>
> **Joshua 10:10**

This was the day "the sun stood still" and Jesus fought for Israel — sending hailstones and slaughtering the enemy usurpers. When the five Southern Coalition kings fled to a cave, Joshua had them captured and instructed the Israelites to put their feet on the necks of their fallen foes — a symbolic picture of the victory of the Seed of The Woman over the Serpent. (Joshua 10:24-25).

33 KINGS – A MYSTERIOUS NUMBER

In the battles for the Promised Land, God and the Israelites exterminated the Nephilim gene pool. No person carrying the Nephilim DNA was to be left. This was the fulfillment of the curse Noah placed on Canaan centuries earlier. Joshua 12 lists all the kings God and the armies of Israel defeated – "all the kings thirty and one," and Moses had defeated Kings Og and Sihon. All told, 33 kings of the Nephilim giant-infested Promised Land were conquered. The number 33 or 1/3 is significant in Scripture because it is associated with the original angelic rebellion against God:

> "And there appeared a great wonder in heaven; a woman clothed with the
> sun, and the moon under her feet, and upon her head a crown of twelve
> stars: And she being with child cried, travailing in birth, and pained to be
> delivered. And there appeared another wonder in heaven; and behold a
> great red dragon, having seven heads and ten horns, and seven crowns
> upon his heads. **And his tail drew the third part of the stars of heaven,**
> **and did cast them to the earth: and the dragon stood before the**
> **woman which was ready to be delivered, for to devour her child as**
> **soon as it was born."**
> **Revelation 12:1–4**

In John's vision of Satan's plan to prevent the birth of the Messiah, the stars the Devil cast to Earth represent the one third of the angels who joined with him in rebellion against God. The post-Flood giants, by the satanic spiritual influence indwelling them, arranged themselves to have 33 rulers among them.

10.   THE LAST STAND OF THE NEPHILIM

CHAPTERS 19-20

Though the Nephilim were conquered by Joshua, small pockets of resistance were not defeated - which proved catastrophic for Israel. The pagan religions of the Nephilim soon infiltrated God's people leading Israel into idolatry - worshiping fallen angels and demons, the spirits of the very giants they had fought against.

KEY THEMES:

- All of the pagan idol worship in the Old Testament can be traced back to the Nephilim.
- The remaining Canaanite nations served as a tool of God's judgment in the book of Judges.
- King David's elite soldiers conquered the final Nephilim in the Promised Land. After their victories, no giant is mentioned again in the Old Testament.

1. Circle the verses which confirm the giants worshipped pagan gods

   Genesis 14:5   Numbers 22:41   1 Samuel 17:43

   1 Samuel 13:10

2. What was distinct about the Israelites who were the first to worship Baal and Ashtaroth? (Judges 2) Check the correct answer(s):

   - They were consumed with lust for money and power _____

   - They kept the pagan traditions of Egypt _____

   - They attempted to create a new tabernacle in their own design_____

   - They were young and did not witness God's miracles in Canaan_____

3. Which passages confirm that God created the "Host of Heaven" that Israel worshiped? Deuteronomy 10:22   Genesis 1:16   Revelation 6:12-13

   Psalm   19:1

4. Read Deuteronomy 18:9-14 and check all the statements that are TRUE:

   - Going to a medium or séance to speak with the dead is a sin

     _____

   - We can use objects like energy crystals or charms when we pray

     _____

   - God gives us strong warnings about the dangers of the occult

     _____

   - Occult practices originated with the Nephilim-led nations

     _____

NEVER FORGET YOU ARE IN A SPIRITUAL BATTLE

In one of Joshua's final addresses to the nation of Israel he posed a choice to the twelve tribes that would determine their destiny in the Promised Land: "choose you this day whom you will serve." The Canaanite enemies were defeated in military battle, but the pagan religions they created still lingered and offered a different kind of threat entirely. After Joshua's death, the nation stopped enforcing the *cherem* – allowing remnants of Canaanites to remain alive and live among them. Instead of eliminating their enemy as God commanded, they instead took tribute from them. (Judges 1:24-30). This act of disobedience allowed the religions of the land to infiltrate The Lord's people.

In Judges chapter 2 a new generation of Israelites – who were not alive to witness the Exodus miracles or God's supernatural victories in the war for the Promised Land, broke off their allegiance to Yahweh and instead worshipped Baal and Ashtaroth. (Judges 2:10-13). While the false god Baal is mentioned many times in Scripture, *Ashtaroth is the first pagan god mentioned in the Bible*: "And in the fourteenth year came Chedorlaomer, and the kings that were with him, and smote the Rephaims in Ashteroth Karnaim" (Genesis 14:5). During the world war of Genesis 14, the Bible records the Rephaim living in a city named in honor of Ashtaroth. The Nephilim were the originators of pagan worship.

The worship of the sun, moon and stars was strictly forbidden in Scripture. The Lord, of course, retains complete authority over the sun, moon, stars, and all the host of heaven. God "made two great lights" (the sun and moon) as well as the stars (Genesis 1:16). He set a "tabernacle for the sun" (Psalm 19:4). The heavens declare the glory of God, their creator (Psalm 19:1). Joshua, trusting in God's power, commanded the sun to "stand still." During the Great Tribulation to come, the Lord will remove the light of the sun, moon, and stars to signal that the end times have commenced (Revelation 6:12–13).

5.   **What were 2 immediate sinful consequences of Israel's failure to root out and remove the Nephilim from the Promised Land as Yahweh commanded? See Judges 3:5-7**

6. What was Henry Shepheard's theory on the origins of grove worship in the land of Canaan?

7. Anything that takes priority in our heart before God is an idol. Whether it's ourselves (spending time on our social media "brand", etc.), approval, hatred, security, success or relationships - when we seek things to give us only what god can give, we are in idolatry. think of idols you may have in your life and write a prayer that God would remove them or put them in their proper place

"And the children of Israel dwelt among the Canaanites, Hittites, and Amorites, and Perizzites, and Hivites, and Jebusites: And they took their daughters to be their wives, and gave their daughters to their sons, and served their gods. And the children of Israel did evil in the sight of the LORD, and forgat the LORD their God, and served Baalim and the groves."

Judges 3:5-7

Forgetting all their history and God's commands, the Israelites intermarried with the remaining descendants of Canaan. Shortly afterwards, that sin led to their adoption of the giants' pagan religions.

Though they were originally used for righteous worship (Genesis 21:33) the groves soon were co-opted by unbelievers in the ancient world to honor demons and fallen angels. The grove was a replica of the Garden of God in Eden. The desire to "reclaim Eden" still burned in the hearts of those who served the Devil. Pagan idols were placed in the midst of the trees of the grove with the hope of conjuring a spirit to receive insight or power. Like all pagan practices grove worship was an attempt to access the heavenly realm without honoring the creator of Heaven. As one commentary on the Garden of Eden stated:

> "It is, therefore morally certain that the Tree or Grove worship found existing in Canaan by Joshua and the Israelites was the same that had been practised there from the very first settlement of the aboriginal Canaanites. But the Canaanites migrated direct from the cradle of the human family — their ancestor Canaan being the grandson of Noah. The origin of Tree and Grove worship in the land of Canaan is thus traced back to the very family who issued from the Ark and to whom all the traditions of Paradise were familiar as household words. Is it possible to believe that it had any other origin but those very traditions?" – *Traditions of Eden: Or, Proofs of the Historical Character of the Pentateuch*, Henry Shepheard, 1871 p. 159.

8. Name 3 idolatrous kings of Israel and their specific sins:

- **King 1:**
- **King 2:**
- **King 3:**

9. What was the ancient significance of "The Valley Of Hinnom"? How did Jesus reference it as a foreshadow of future judgment?

ISRAEL'S DESIRE FOR A KING LED TO GREATER SPIRITUAL CALAMITY

"But the thing displeased Samuel, when they said, Give us a king to judge us. And Samuel prayed unto the LORD. **And the LORD said unto Samuel, Hearken unto the voice of the people in all that they say unto thee: for they have not rejected thee, but they have rejected me, that I should not reign over them**. According to all the works which they have done since the day that I brought them up out of Egypt even unto this day, wherewith they have forsaken me, and served other gods, so do they also unto thee."

Samuel 8:6–8

Despite the prophet's warning that appointing a king would have disastrous consequences, the Israelites insisted on appointing a monarch (1 Samuel 8:11–18). King Saul, the first human king of the 12 tribes, was an unrepentant man of dubious faith. His reckless actions and defiance of God led him ultimately to consult with a witch (1 Samuel 28:7).

The entire history of both the Northern and Southern kingdom's rulers is littered with men who led the nation away from The Lord and into worship of the demonic realm:

- King Solomon, who descended into spiritual rebellion through marriage – as he had over 700 wives and 300 concubines. Many of these women lured him into idolatry. His brazen defiance led the nation of Israel splitting into two kingdoms – the northern and southern division of tribes.

- Jeroboam, the first king of the northern tribes, was so wicked that he erected golden calves and told his people "behold thy gods, O Israel, which brought thee up out of the land of Egypt" (1 Kings 12:28).

- During the reign of Rehoboam, the southern kingdom: "…also built them high places, and images, and groves, on every high hill, and under every green tree. And there were also sodomites in the land: **and they did according to all the abominations of the nations which the LORD cast out before the children of Israel**." (1 Kings 14:21–24),

By the time Manasseh, the final king of Judah was in power, the Lord's patience with His people was approaching its limit. The Northern kingdom had already been conquered by the Assyrian empire. Manasseh brought judgment onto the Southern kingdom by engaging in every occult practice forbidden by God, even sacrificing his own children. On top of that satanic act, he set a graven image in the temple – an eerie foreshadow of the abomination of desolation. (2 Kings 21:1-9). Soon the Southern Kingdom would fall to the Babylonian empire and the first temple would be destroyed. The Devil could not defeat Israel on the battlefield via the Nephilim, but their religion brought utter ruin to the twelve tribes.

Manasseh's child sacrifice took place in the valley of the son of Hinnom, a location for a great deal of occult activity and murder in the Old Testament. (2 Chronicles 28:1-3). Several centuries earlier, it was known as the valley of the Rephaim.

The Valley of the Son of Hinnom was an ancient stronghold for the Canaanites. The idolatry the giants left behind was so alluring that it dragged the people of Israel into brazen rebellion against God and ultimately their loss of the Promised Land. The Valley of the Son of Hinnom, or *ge enna* in Greek, had a specific place of sacrifice called Tophet. It is believed to have derived its name from the Hebrew word *toph*, or drum. Loud drums were played to drown out the cries of children being sacrificed in Tophet's fire. Gehenna soon became synonymous with Hell itself in Scripture.

In the New Testament, the Lord Jesus Christ referenced "Gehenna" on 12 occasions. For example:

"But I say unto you, That whosoever is angry with his brother without a cause shall be in danger of the judgment: and whosoever shall say to his brother, Raca, shall be in danger of the council: but whosoever shall say, Thou fool, shall be in danger of hell [*ge enna*] fire."

Matthew 5:22

"And if thy hand offend thee, cut it off: it is better for thee to enter into life maimed, than having two hands to go into hell [*ge enna*], into the fire that never shall be quenched...."

Mark 9:43

THE LAST STAND OF THE NEPHILIM

10. **David's duel versus Goliath was a powerful foreshadow of the end times battle between the two bloodlines. List 4 similarities between the David and The Lord *Yeshua*, The Messiah**

11. **"And Ishbibenob, _____ _____, the weight of whose spear weighed three hundred shekels of brass in weight, he being girded with a new sword, _____ _____." - 2 Samuel 21:16**

12. **Who were the 4 giants killed by David's Mighty Men?**

13. **What did Satan do after the death of the Egyptian? What does this event say to you about the spiritual warfare you face in your own life?**

King David stands as one of the greatest foreshadows of The Lord Jesus Christ. Here are just several of the numerous similarities between the life of David and The Lord during His first Advent:

- David was of the tribe of Judah – the tribe from which Jesus Christ was born.

- David in Hebrew means "beloved." When Jesus was baptized in the Jordan River, God the Father spoke from Heaven and called Jesus "my beloved son."

- David was born in Bethlehem (Ruth 4:18-22; 1 Samuel 16). Jesus was born in Bethlehem (Luke 2:4).

- Several Old Testament Messianic prophecies used the name "David" to refer to Jesus. For example, Ezekiel 37:25: "And they shall dwell in the land that I have given unto Jacob my servant, wherein your fathers have dwelt; and they shall dwell therein, even they, and their children, and their children's children for ever: **and my servant David shall be their prince for ever**." Among other passages are Jeremiah 30:9; Ezekiel 34:23; Ezekiel 34:24; Ezekiel 37:24; Hosea 3:5.

- Prior to becoming king, David worked as a shepherd. Jesus called Himself the "good Shepherd" (John 10:11; 10:14).

- David was 30 years old when he began to reign as king (2 Samuel 5:4). Jesus was 30 years old when He began His earthly ministry (Luke 3:3).

So it should be little surprise that the servant of God who slew a Nephilim as a child, would lead the final assault that eliminated the giants in the Promised Land for good. David's "mighty men" – elite soldiers who were closest to the king, defeated the final remnant of Nephilim. The giant Ishbibenob attempted to kill David on the battlefield prompting the king's soldier Abishai to slay that Nephilim. From there the mighty men told David to remain off the field of battle and allow them to fight for him. And in rapid succession, they eradicated the final giants mentioned in the Bible:

> "And it came to pass after this, that there was again a battle with the Philistines at Gob: then Sibbechai the Hushathite slew Saph, which was of the sons of the giant. And there was again a battle in Gob with the Philistines, where Elhanan the son of Jaareoregim, a Bethlehemite, slew the brother of Goliath the Gittite, the staff of whose spear was like a weaver's beam. And there was yet a battle in Gath, where was a man of great stature, that had on every hand six fingers, and on every foot six toes, four and twenty in number; and he also was born to the giant. And when he defied Israel, Jonathan the son of Shimeah the brother of David slew him. These four were born to the giant in Gath, and fell by the hand of David, and by the hand of his servants."
> **2 Samuel 21:18–22**

Benaiah, one of David's valiant warriors, had the honor of killing the last giant mentioned in Scripture – "the Egyptian." (1 Chronicles 11:22-24). He was 8 feet nine inches tall (using the Egyptian cubit), and, like Goliath and his kin, carried a spear the size of a weaver's beam. His death provoked Satan to counterstrike.

With his supermen exterminated, the Devil took direct action against Israel, tempting David to count his military forces. This was an act of vanity and pride in his own power. The Lord had delivered David and the 12 tribes through all their military conflicts. For David then to engage in such a pointless exercise was an insult to the Lord. Israel suffered through a plague that killed 70,000 men because of David's sin (1 Chronicles 21:14). The Devil was forced into new tactics as the Nephilim were finally destroyed. This was also the end of any Philistine military aggression in Israel's history.

14. "When the_____, he walketh through dry places, seeking rest; and finding none, he saith, _____

_____." – Matthew 12:43-45

15. What are the Hebrew words for "demon" (or "devils") and "angel"? Provide examples of verses that contain each word.

16. "They provoked him to jealousy with _____, with abominations provoked they him to anger. They sacrificed _____, not to God; to gods whom they knew not, _____, whom your fathers feared not." - Deuteronomy 32:16-17

17. Circle True or False for each of the following statements: The Genesis 6 angels are the demons later in Scripture (Jude 1:6-7).   TRUE   FALSE

The 2 angels with Jesus literally ate the food prepared by Abraham (Genesis 18:1-8).   TRUE   FALSE

Jesus explained to the disciples that spirits have flesh and bones like humans (Luke 24:39).   TRUE   FALSE

Demons can bestow supernatural power to humans that they possess (Acts 16:16-18).　　　TRUE　　　FALSE

18. Read Psalm 106:36-38 and Isaiah 26:13-14 and 1 Corinthians 10:19-21. What was the agenda of demons in ancient times? What is their mission in modern times?

Demons and fallen angels are different beings. The fallen angels (*malak* in Hebrew) were created by God before the creation of Earth (Job 38). The demons (*sed* or *shedim* in Hebrew) are the spirits of the Nephilim, and thus descendants of the Genesis 6 apostate angels who were imprisoned in the abyss.

Scripture provides clear evidence of the differences between angels and demons:

- Angels have bodies – Demons do not – The angels who visited Abraham's home ate his dinner and had their feet cleaned by his servants. (Genesis 18).

  Demons, on the other hand, do not have bodies. In the Old Testament they are referred to as "familiar spirits." In the New Testament they are called "unclean spirits." To prove He was truly resurrected to a glorified body the Lord Jesus Christ told His disciples, "Behold my hands and my feet, that it is I myself: handle me, and see; *for a spirit hath not flesh and bones*, as ye see me have" (Luke 24:39). All through the Gospels, demons desperately seek bodies of human beings to inhabit, and sometimes hundreds of them occupy the body of one person.

THE DEMONIC AGENDA – LURING HUMANITY INTO IDOLATRY

Demons are connected to occult activity throughout the Bible. When King Saul consulted a witch to try and communicate with the spirit of the deceased prophet Samuel, he went to a woman in Endor who had "a familiar spirit." (1 Samuel 28:7-8). In the book of Acts, the Apostle Paul encountered a young woman who was making money for her masters by "divination" or fortune-telling. She had literal power that was bestowed by a demon who Paul was able to exorcise from the woman and return her to her right mind. (Acts 16:16-18).

In ancient Israel, it was the deceased spirits of the giants that took on the role of the "gods" in the postdiluvian world. Isaiah 26:13-14 contains a portion of a song of confession in which the Israelites tell God:

> "O LORD our God, other lords beside thee have had dominion over us:
> but by thee only will we make mention of thy name. They are dead
> [*Rephaim*], they shall not live; they are deceased, they shall not rise:
> therefore hast thou visited and destroyed them, and made all their memory
> to perish."
> **Isaiah 26:13-14**

Not only does the passage confess that demons were ruling over Israel, but it specifically refers to them as "Rephaim" – the sprits of the dead Nephilim. Psalm 106:36 identifies these false gods as "the idols of Canaan."

In the New Testament, the agenda of demons remained the same – impersonating false gods and instigating humanity to sin. The Apostle Paul confirmed this:

> "What say I then? that the idol is any thing, or that which is offered in
> sacrifice to idols is any thing? **But I say, that the things which the**
> **Gentiles sacrifice, they sacrifice to devils**, and not to God: and I would
> not that ye should have fellowship with devils. Ye cannot drink the cup of

the Lord, and the cup of devils: ye cannot be partakers of the Lord's table, and of the table of devils."

1 Corinthians 10:19–21

DISCERNMENT – WHAT WE NEED TO AVOID FALSE TEACHINGS

"Beloved, believe not every spirit, but try the spirits whether they are of God: because many false prophets are gone out into the world."

John 4:1

Demons seek to spiritually corrupt humanity and lead them into idolatry. The many false teachers and heretics who preach erroneous doctrines while using the name of the Lord Jesus Christ are under the control or influence of demonic spirits (the spirits "seduce" these false preachers, again using the sexual language often associated with the Nephilim).

19. **What are 3 "doctrines of demons" that are taught in churches today? Explain how they do not align with Scripture**

20. **What are some occult and New Age trends today that are luring people to interact with the demonic realm? How can we combat this?**

11. JESUS CHRIST AND THE NEPHILIM

CHAPTERS 21 AND 22

When the demons encountered Jesus Christ during His first Advent, they knew precisely who He was: The Messiah. How did they know? Because He was the one who conquered them in the wars for the Promised Land and will sentence them to their permanent judgment at His Return.

KEY THEMES:

- Jesus' ability to command, control and terrify the demons served as a stunning proof that He indeed was the prophesied Messiah.
- After His death on the cross, Jesus descended into the abyss to proclaim His victory to the Genesis 6 apostate angels.
- All believers will one day receive their own immortal, heavenly-realm bodies and will be the new "Sons of God", ruling and reigning with Christ for eternity.

EVEN THE DEMONS BELIEVE – AND TREMBLE

1. "Saying, Let us alone; what have we to do with thee, thou Jesus of Nazareth? art thou come to destroy us? I_____ _____" - Luke 4:34

2. Why were the demons so frightened when they saw The Lord Jesus Christ? How did they know who He was?

3. Read Mark 5:1-13 and Luke 8:30-31. What are 4 allusions to the Judgment Of The Nephilim found in the account of the demon-possessed man in the Gadarenes?

4. How does the unpardonable sin relate to the Judgment Of The Nephilim?

5. Provide 2 examples from Scripture where Jesus' power over demons immediately led some to consider him the Messiah.

In the days of Jesus Christ's incarnation on Earth, there was an astounding amount of demonic activity. Whether they were called "unclean spirits" or "devils," these disembodied spirits had a number of encounters with the Lord and always knew His true identity:

> "And unclean spirits, when they saw him, fell down before him, and cried, saying, Thou art the Son of God. And he straitly charged them that they should not make him known."
>
> **Mark 3:11–12**

These Nephilim spirits trembled with fear because they knew they were confronting the Angel Of The Lord who conquered them in the days of the war for the Promised Land. The demons immediately recognized Jesus as "the Holy One" a title used to signify Jesus Christ as both God and Messiah (2 Kings 19:22; Psalm 16:10; Psalm 89:18). Christ eradicated the original Nephilim with the flood and unleashed divine war against their postdiluvian descendants. This is why they responded to His every command and questioned if He was coming to "destroy" them once more.

In the account of the demoniac in the country of the Gadarenes, there are several allusions to the Judgment of the Nephilim:

- The Gadarenes were located in what was once Bashan, the home of legendary Rephaim king Og.

- The possessed man, like a giant, was so supernaturally strong that "no man could bind him, no not with chains." (Mark 5:1-5). The sinning Sons of God who fathered the Nephilim were bound with chains in the abyss where they remain today until the judgment of the great day. (Jude 1:6-7).

- The demoniac displayed constant rage and sinful insanity, cutting himself with stones. Once the Nephilim took over the preflood world, their ensuing corruption filled the world with violence. (Genesis 6).

- When Christ questioned the demons, they pleaded with The Lord to not send them to "the deep":

"And Jesus asked him, saying, What is thy name? And he said, Legion: because many devils were entered into him. And they besought him that he would not command them to go out into the deep."
Luke 8:30–31

The demons were aware of the exact location of the prison of their fallen angelic forefathers and begged Jesus to spare them the same punishment.

- After the demons pleaded to be sent into pigs (ritually unclean animals) The Lord obliged. The herd charged "violently" into a deep portion of the sea and drowned. This was a reenactment of the flood judgment where the giants perished by drowning in the waters of the flood for 150 days.

Jesus' absolute authority over demons and their terror when they encountered Him served another critical purpose: it was a powerful and dynamic witness that He indeed was the Messiah and the fulfillment of Genesis 3:15:

"As they went out, behold, they brought to him a dumb man possessed with a devil. And when the devil was cast out, the dumb spake: **and the multitudes marvelled, saying, It was never so seen in Israel.**"
Matthew 9:32–33

"Then was brought unto him one possessed with a devil, blind, and dumb: and he healed him, insomuch that the blind and dumb both spake and saw. **And all the people were amazed, and said, Is not this the son of David?**"
Matthew 12:22–23

THE UNPARDONABLE SIN – NEW TESTAMENT VERSION OF THE CHEREM

The birth of Christ was the ultimate victory over Satan's attempt to prevent the Messiah's Advent. For 4,000 years of history, Satan attempted to corrupt and pollute the lineage of the Messiah. All the genealogies in Scripture testify to his grand failure to do so. As to His humanity, Jesus Christ was born of a wholly human bloodline. To slander the Savior of humanity with an accusation that He, the Creator of all, was possessed by the spirit of a dead giant, was a sin that would receive no pardon.

THE SAVIOR VISITED THE ANGELS WHO SINNED IN HELL

6. **"For Christ also hath once suffered for sins, the just for the unjust, that he might bring us to God, being put to death in the flesh, but quickened by the Spirit: By which also he went_____**

    _____

    _____, that is, eight souls were saved by water."
    - 1 Peter 3:18-20

7. **What was Reverend R.A. Torrey's interpretation of 1 Peter 3:18-20?**

A startling account that you will only find in the Bible and no other apocryphal or extra-Biblical text, is that of Jesus going to the abyss to proclaim His victory on the cross to the Genesis 6 fallen angels. The New Testament has two Greek words translated as "preach" in the King James Version. *Kērussō,* the word used in the above verse, means "to be a herald, officiate as a herald."

Reverend R.A. Torrey concurred that the "spirits" Jesus visited were indeed the apostate B'nai Ha Elohim:

> "Many commentators understand the descendants of Seth, a godly man, to be "the sons of God" in this passage. But if we are to interpret Scripture by Scripture they seem rather to have been angelic beings. There seems to be a clear reference to this passage in Jude 6, where we are told of 'angels which kept not their own principality but left their proper habitation' and in consequence were kept in everlasting chains in darkness until the judgment of the great day...."
> – *Difficulties in the Bible, Alleged Errors and Contradictions,* Rev. R.A. Torrey, Moody Press, 1907.

THE RETURN OF THE SONS OF GOD – ALL BELIEVERS RECEIVE IMMORTALITY THROUGH JESUS CHRIST

8. **What does 1 John 3:1-2 reveal about your ultimate destiny? What are your feelings about being "like Jesus"? What does that mean to you?**

The immortality Satan promised Adam and Eve could never be achieved through human effort. It could be attained only through Jesus Christ. And in salvation, a new generation of sons of God were raised up, all born-again Christians. The sinful angels of the original satanic rebellion were to be replaced with the newly born sons of God. If you are a born-again believer this is who you are today.

"But if the Spirit of him that raised up Jesus from the dead dwell in you, he that raised up Christ from the dead shall also quicken your mortal bodies by his Spirit that dwelleth in you."

Romans 8:11

Your ultimate destiny is to be glorified and perfected in Jesus Christ - in spirit and body. At Christ's return, all believers will have an immortal, celestial body prepared for eternity with the Savior. God wants us to be one with Him (John 17:22-23). We only need to believe and trust Him.

9. **Read Daniel 2:43. in light of this study, what are your thoughts on this prophecy? how do you see this prophecy being fulfilled in the end times?**

FINAL THOUGHTS AND REFLECTIONS

How has this study affected your view of God? Has the supernatural interpretation of Genesis 6 changed your perspective on the Bible, spiritual warfare or your walk with God? Share these thoughts below.

COPYRIGHT NOTICE

WANT ACCESS TO MORE RESOURCES?
Visit JUDGMENTOFTHENEPHILIM.COM

- ***Judgment Of The Nephilim: Secrets Of The Preflood World DVD***: The documentary version of the best-selling book is here! An overview of ***Judgment Of The Nephilim*** with narration and exclusive commentary by Ryan Pitterson.

- ***The Final Nephilim***: The long-awaited sequel to ***Judgment Of The Nephilim***! ***The Final Nephilim*** details the rise of Antichrist - the "other Seed" of Genesis 3:15 - who is The Final Nephilim. Prepare for an exciting study of Revelation leading to the final confrontation at Armageddon.

- ***The Final Nephilim Study Guide***: The companion Study Guide to ***The Final Nephilim***. Excellent for grasping the research that went into the book and for group study.

- ***The Final Nephilim: Battle For Heaven And Earth*** **DVD**: The documentary of The Final Nephilim goes from Genesis to Revelation as Ryan Pitterson unravels the mysteries of Revelation, explores the UFO Phenomena, quantum physics and much more!

Made in United States
Orlando, FL
08 August 2022

20727583R00078